INORGANIC SYNTHESES

VOLUME III

mdg

EDITOR-IN-CHIEF

Jacob Kleinberg   *The University of Kansas*

ASSOCIATE EDITORS

Eugene O. Brimm   *Linde Company*

George H. Cady   *University of Washington*

Francis P. Dwyer   *John Curtin School of Medical Research,
Australian National University*

Henry F. Holtzclaw, Jr.   *University of Nebraska*

William L. Jolly   *University of California (Berkeley)*

Joseph J. Katz   *Argonne National Laboratory*

Morris L. Nielsen   *Monsanto Chemical Co.*

Lowell E. Netherton   *Victor Chemical Works*

Robert W. Parry   *University of Michigan*

Janet D. Scott, *Wingdale, N.Y.*

S. Young Tyree, Jr.   *University of North Carolina*

Geoffrey Wilkinson   *Imperial College of Science & Technology*

Earl L. Muetterties   *E. I. du Pont de Nemours & Company*

Inorganic Syntheses

Volume III

EDITOR-IN-CHIEF

LUDWIG F. AUDRIETH
University of Illinois

ASSOCIATE EDITORS

JOHN C. BAILAR, JR.
University of Illinois

HAROLD S. BOOTH
Western Reserve University

W. CONARD FERNELIUS
The Pennsylvania State College

WALTER C. SCHUMB
Massachusetts Institute of Technology

RALPH C. YOUNG
Massachusetts Institute of Technology

CONSULTANT ON NOMENCLATURE AND INDEXING

JANET D. SCOTT
The Interscience Encyclopedia, Inc., Brooklyn

ADVISORY BOARD

ARTHUR A. BLANCHARD
Massachusetts Institute of Technology

W. C. JOHNSON
University of Chicago

RAYMOND E. KIRK
The Polytechnic Institute of Brooklyn

First Edition
Second Impression

New York   Toronto   London
McGraw-Hill Book Company
1950

INORGANIC SYNTHESES, VOLUME III

To

the countless unknown but valiant
soldiers of science upon whose labors
Inorganic Syntheses are based, this
series of volumes is dedicated in the
hope that it will ease the toil of future
legions.

PREFACE

The Board of Editors of INORGANIC SYNTHESES has been more than pleased with the reception accorded to Volumes I and II of this series. The importance of inorganic chemistry as a distinctive branch of chemistry, so clearly defined by developments in the Second World War, has not only encouraged and stimulated the Editorial Board to continue its efforts to make available tried and tested procedures for the preparation of inorganic compounds, but has demonstrated beyond question the need for information of the sort presented in these volumes. The very fact that almost half of the syntheses contained in the present volume were submitted by, or checked in, industrial laboratories is evidence of the usefulness of these volumes.

The policies and practices established as the result of experience gained in assembling Volumes I and II have been continued. Each procedure has been checked carefully at some laboratory other than the one from which the original method was submitted. After checking and revision, syntheses were edited and then returned to the original authors for final approval. No synthesis is published until such approval by the authors has been granted.

As in the past, the syntheses have been arranged on the basis of the Mendeleev periodic classification. An effort has also been made to follow the system of nomenclature adopted in the preparation of Volume II. Trivial and common names, if widely used in the chemical literature, may have been used in a few cases, especially in the index. To make it possible to use all three volumes more satisfactorily, the index has been set up on a cumulative basis.

It has been felt desirable to continue the policy of presenting brief survey articles dealing with specific subjects of interest in the field of inorganic chemistry. It has also been felt desirable to bridge the gap between inorganic and organic chemistry by presenting syntheses of materials which, though organic in nature, are widely used by inorganic chemists.

Contributions are now being accepted for publication in Volume IV of this series. All manuscripts, in triplicate, should be sent directly to Professor John C. Bailar, Jr., of the University of Illinois, who will serve as editor-in-chief of Volume IV. In submitting manuscripts, the authors are specifically requested to adhere to the style employed in the publication of the first three volumes. The procedure should be preceded by an introduction and followed by a discussion of physical and chemical properties of the compound whose method of preparation has been described. Where analytical methods are sufficiently distinctive to warrant a more extended exposition, detailed directions should also be included. Pertinent references should be placed at the end of the synthesis.

The editors take great pleasure in announcing the election of Professor E. G. Rochow of Harvard University and Professor G. Therald Moeller of the University of Illinois to membership on the Editorial Board. Janet Scott has accepted membership on the Board, after having served so faithfully and conscientiously as consultant on nomenclature and indexing for Volumes II and III.

The editor-in-chief is most grateful to his associates on the Editorial Board and to members of the Advisory Board for their help in the preparation of Volume III. It is also a pleasure to acknowledge the help of Patricia Schloesser and Betty Jane Ogg in the preparation of the manuscript.

The editors will be grateful if readers and users of this and previous volumes will call to their attention any errors or omissions.

LUDWIG F. AUDRIETH

URBANA, ILL.
March, 1950

CONTENTS

ix

CHAPTER V

CHAPTER VI

CHAPTER VII

CHAPTER VIII

CHAPTER VIII

CHAPTER I

1. SODIUM PEROXIDE 8-HYDRATE

SUBMITTED BY R. A. PENNEMAN*
CHECKED BY A. D. F. TOY†

Hydrates of sodium peroxide may be prepared by (1) the slow evaporation of a cold aqueous solution of sodium peroxide;[1] (2) the slow action of water vapor on solid sodium peroxide;[2] (3) the electrolysis of aqueous sodium hydroxide at temperatures between −10 and 0°,[3] and (4) precipitation from a cold solution of sodium hydroxide and hydrogen peroxide by means of alcohol.[4]

The method outlined below is a modification of the last mentioned of these procedures and yields a chemically pure product. The success of this method depends upon the use of an excess of sodium hydroxide, since no precipitate is

* University of Illinois, Urbana, Ill.
† Victor Chemical Works Research Laboratory, Chicago Heights, Ill.

obtained when hydrogen peroxide is present in excess. However, it was found that the amount of water in the hydrate depends upon the temperature at which precipitation is carried out. The directions that follow give the 8-hydrate consistently, whereas a product analyzing almost exactly for $Na_2O_2 \cdot 11H_2O$ is formed when hydrogen peroxide is added to a saturated sodium hydroxide solution at 0°.

Procedure

Ten grams of carbonate-free sodium hydroxide is dissolved in 25 ml. of water in a stoppered Erlenmeyer flask and cooled to 15°. Ten grams of a 30 per cent solution of hydrogen peroxide (corresponding to a mol ratio of NaOH: $H_2O_2 = 2.83 : 1$) is added slowly with constant stirring at a rate such that the temperature does not rise above 18°. Sixty milliliters of 95 per cent alcohol (cooled to 15°) is added; the flask is then stoppered and shaken vigorously. The solution is allowed to stand about ½ hour, the supernatant liquid is decanted, and the washing is repeated with two 60-ml. portions of cold alcohol. The white crystals are filtered with suction on a hardened filter paper and washed with ether. The compound is transferred quickly to a desiccator containing sulfuric acid (not *in vacuo*) and kept in a cold chest for 10 hours at a temperature not above 15°. The yield is 18 g. (92 per cent based on H_2O_2). The product may be preserved for a limited period of time in the ice chest.

Analysis

Sodium (reported as Na_2O) was determined by hydrolysis of a sample and titration with a standard acid. Peroxide oxygen was determined by dissolving a weighed sample in an excess of standard cerium(IV) nitrate solution and titrating the excess cerium(IV) ion with iron(II) sulfate using *o*-phenanthroline as indicator.[5] *Anal.* Calcd. for $Na_2O_2 \cdot 8H_2O$: Na_2O, 27.88; O (peroxide) 7.2. Found: Na_2O, 27.92; O, 7.11.

Properties

The 8-hydrate is a white, crystalline powder which reacts readily with carbon dioxide, hence must be kept from contact with the atmosphere. It melts in its own water of crystallization at 30° and decomposes to yield oxygen. If kept for a long period over sulfuric acid in a vacuum desiccator, the 8-hydrate loses 6 molecules of water to form the 2-hydrate, $Na_2O_2 \cdot 2H_2O$.[2]

References

1. HARCOURT: *J. Chem. Soc.*, **14**, 278 (1862).
2. JOUBERT: *Compt. rend.*, **132**, 86 (1901).
3. German patent 245531 (1911).
4. FAIRLY: *J. Chem. Soc.*, **31**, 125 (1877).
5. WALDEN, HAMMETT, and CHAPMAN: *J. Am. Chem. Soc.*, **53**, 3908 (1931).

CHAPTER II

2. BASIC BERYLLIUM DERIVATIVES OF ORGANIC ACIDS

By Therald Moeller*

An apparently unique property of beryllium is its tendency to form so-called "basic" derivatives of a number of organic acids. These compounds correspond in composition to the general formula $Be_4O(RCOO)_6$ (R = hydrogen or organic radical) and are, in general, remarkably stable. In fact, the tendency toward their formation is so pronounced that the corresponding "normal" beryllium salts can be prepared only with difficulty or not at all. Best known of these compounds is the basic acetate, a material that was first discussed critically by Urbain and Lacombe[1] in 1901. A number of other compounds of the series have been described by Lacombe,[2] Tanatar and Kurowski,[3] Glassmann,[4] Bragg and Morgan,[5] Morgan and Astbury,[6] and Feild.[9] A comprehensive summary of the preparation and properties of these substances is given in Gmelin's "Handbuch der anorganischen Chemie."[7]

Preparation. Listed methods of preparation are most extensive for the basic acetate. Methods for the preparation of this compound, however, are generally applicable to the other members of the series.

1. Action of Organic Acid on Beryllium Oxide or Hydroxide. This method has been used for the preparation of the majority of the basic derivatives, the most notable exception being the formate. Usually, it amounts to treatment of the hydroxide with the appropriate acid, heating until reaction is complete, evaporating to a solid or oily product,

* University of Illinois, Urbana, Ill.

extracting the basic beryllium compound with a solvent such as chloroform or petroleum ether, and crystallizing from that solvent.

2. Action of Organic Acid on Beryllium Carbonate or Basic Carbonate. This method is similar in all respects to the above procedure. While it has been used most extensively for only the simpler members of the series, there is no apparent reason why it should not be equally effective for the preparation of other members as well. The procedure is one of the few claimed to give the basic formate.[2, 3] Directions given for the preparation of the basic acetate (synthesis 3) and basic propionate (synthesis 3) represent modifications of this general procedure.

3. Action of Organic Acid or Anhydride on Anhydrous Beryllium Chloride. This method apparently yields only the normal formate but gives basic beryllium derivatives of such acids as acetic, propionic, butyric, benzoic, and o-chlorobenzoic.[8, 9] It amounts to refluxing anhydrous beryllium chloride with the corresponding acid or anhydride, adding benzene, toluene, or petroleum ether, and distilling to remove the hydrogen chloride and acid chloride by-products. Under strictly anhydrous conditions normal beryllium derivatives are said to result,[9] but in the presence of water, added either with the original acid or as moist benzene, the basic derivatives are formed.

4. Action of Organic Acid Chloride on a Basic Beryllium Compound. This method is useful for the preparation of mixed basic beryllium derivatives. Thus, refluxing basic beryllium isobutyrate with acetyl chloride yields a mixed compound,[3] the composition of which may be represented by the formula $Be_4O(CH_3COO)_2 \cdot [(CH_3)_2CHCOO]_4$. A mixed acetate propionate of composition $Be_4O(CH_3COO)_3$-$(CH_3CH_2COO)_3$ has been prepared from the basic propionate by the same procedure.[3, 5]

5. Miscellaneous. Preparations of the basic formate by heating the normal formate under reduced pressure (30 to 35 mm.) and by boiling the normal formate with a water suspension containing the calculated amount of beryllium carbonate have been described.[3]

In addition to the compounds listed in Table I, corresponding basic derivatives of the following acids have been reported: crotonic; isocrotonic; levulinic; succinic; cyanoacetic; mono-, di-, and trichloroacetic; monobromoacetic; monochloro- and monobromopropionic; lactic; glycolic; ethyl- and phenylglycolic (α-hydroxybutyric and mandelic, respectively); and salicylic. Confirmatory evidence for the identities of most of these is completely lacking.

Properties. The basic beryllium compounds are nonelectrolytes and possess all of the properties of purely covalent substances. They are low-melting, low-boiling materials that generally sublime or distill without decomposition. They are usually insoluble in water but soluble in such organic solvents as chloroform, ether, petroleum ether, benzene, toluene, and the alcohols. Physical constants, where known, are given in Table I. Molecular weights, as determined by vapor density[1] and cryoscopic[2,3] measurements, correspond to those of monomolecular compounds of composition $Be_4O(RCOO)_6$.

Chemically, the basic beryllium compounds are stable toward heat, toward oxidation except under very drastic conditions (*e.g.*, boiling with nitric acid), and toward cold water. Treatment with boiling water usually effects hydrolysis slowly; treatment with mineral acids normally yields the corresponding beryllium salt and the free organic acid.

Structure. Older concepts picturing the basic beryllium compounds as derivatives of condensed acids or as structural analogs of the true basic salts of the other elements have been discarded in favor of unitary structures comparable with those ascribed to other strictly covalent compounds.

The x-ray studies of Bragg and Morgan[5] on the basic acetate indicate a central oxygen atom surrounded tetrahedrally by the four beryllium atoms, each edge of the

TABLE I. PROPERTIES OF BASIC BERYLLIUM DERIVATIVES

Derivative	Formula	Melting point, °C	Boiling point, °C	Density, g./ml.
Formate	$Be_4O(HCOO)_6$	Sublimes	330–331	1.39
Acetate	$Be_4O(CH_3COO)_6$	285–286	339–341 (19 mm.)	1.25
Propionate	$Be_4O(CH_3CH_2COO)_6$	137.5–138	330	
Triacetate Tripropionate	$Be_4O(CH_3COO)_3(CH_3CH_2COO)_3$	140–142	239 (19 mm.)	
Butyrate	$Be_4O(CH_3CH_2CH_2COO)_6$	25–27	336–337	1.14
Isobutyrate	$Be_4O[(CH_3)_2CHCOO]_6$	88–89	351	
Diacetate Tetraisobutyrate	$Be_4O(CH_3COO)_2[(CH_3)_2CHCOO]_4$	–15	254 (19 mm.)	
Isovalerate	$Be_4O[(CH_3)_2CHCH_2COO]_6$	......	......	
Pivalate	$Be_4O[(CH_3)_3CCOO]_6$	163	......	1.05
Benzoate	$Be_4O(C_6H_5COO)_6$	317–318		
o-Chlorobenzoate	$Be_4O(ClC_6H_4COO)_6$	255–256		

tetrahedron being occupied by an acetate group acting as a bridge between two atoms of beryllium. This structural arrangement may be depicted graphically in the following manner:

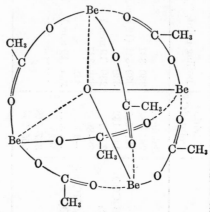

The data of Morgan and Astbury[6] are in agreement with this picture. Pauling and Sherman[10] indicate the structure to amount to four BeO_4 tetrahedra with one oxygen atom common to all four and the remaining oxygen atoms being supplied by the acetate groups. This is essentially the same concept.

X-ray studies[5,6] also indicate that the same type of structure may be assigned to the basic propionate, triacetate tripropionate, isobutyrate, butyrate, and pivalate. It may therefore be assumed as general for all members of the series. In the basic formate and acetate, complete crystal symmetry is predicted by structures of this type. Replacement of the hydrogen or methyl with radicals such as ethyl and propyl should induce dissymmetry. That this is true is shown by the crystal habits of these compounds. The basic acetate crystallizes in the cubic system, but the basic propionate, triacetate tripropionate, and pivalate are monoclinic in form, and the basic isobutyrate crystallizes in the triclinic system. The low melting point of the basic butyrate made a complete x-ray investigation difficult, but the crystals were shown to be of very low symmetry.[6]

References

1. URBAIN and LACOMBE: *Compt. rend.*, **133**, 874 (1901).
2. LACOMBE: *ibid.*, **134**, 772 (1902).
3. TANATAR and KUROWSKI: *J. Russ. Phys. Chem. Soc.*, **39**, 936 (1907).
4. GLASSMANN: *Ber.*, **41**, 33 (1908).
5. BRAGG and MORGAN: *Proc. Roy. Soc. (London)*, **A104**, 437 (1923).
6. MORGAN and ASTBURY: *ibid.*, **A112**, 441 (1926).
7. GMELIN: "Handbuch der anorganischen Chemie," No. 26, pp. 150–155, Verlag Chemie, G.m.b.H., Berlin, 1930.
8. FUNK and RÖMER: *Z. anorg. allgem. Chem.*, **239**, 288 (1938).
9. FEILD: *J. Am. Chem. Soc.*, **61**, 1817 (1939).
10. PAULING and SHERMAN: *Proc. Nat. Acad. Sci.*, **20**, 340 (1934).

3. BASIC BERYLLIUM ACETATE AND PROPIONATE

$$xBeO \cdot yBeCO_3 + \frac{3}{2}(x + y)RCOOH \rightarrow$$

$$\frac{x + y}{4} Be_4O(RCOO)_6 + yCO_2 + \frac{3}{4}(x + y)H_2O$$

SUBMITTED BY THERALD MOELLER,* ALVIN J. COHEN,* AND ELLIOT MARVELL*

CHECKED BY P. S. BAKER† AND D. F. SMITH†

The basic acetate and propionate of beryllium are prepared most conveniently from a reactive form of the basic carbonate. The composition and the reactivity of the starting material are variable, and it may therefore be necessary to prepare the so-called "basic" carbonate from some convenient source of beryllium, especially if the available "carbonate" dissolves with difficulty in either hot acetic or propionic acid. For properties of these compounds see page 7.

Procedure

A. BASIC BERYLLIUM ACETATE

$$Be_4O(CH_3COO)_6$$

Forty grams of basic beryllium carbonate is stirred with 80 ml. of glacial acetic acid on the hot plate until carbon

* University of Illinois, Urbana, Ill.
† University of Vermont, Burlington, Vt.

dioxide is no longer evolved.* When reaction is complete, some of the basic acetate may separate as white, semitransparent crystals. If reaction is incomplete, an amorphous-appearing white residue remains. The solution is cooled to room temperature, and the crude basic beryllium acetate that crystallizes is removed by suction filtration and air-dried. The product is treated with 60 to 80 ml. of chloroform and any undissolved material removed by filtration. The chloroform solution is evaporated on the steam bath. The colorless octahedra of the basic acetate are freed of residual solvent in a vacuum desiccator. The product melts at 284° (uncorr.) and sublimes without residue under reduced pressure. The yield is 28 g. (65 per cent, based upon a basic carbonate containing 26.6 per cent beryllium oxide).† Anal. Calcd. for $Be_4O(CH_3COO)_6$: C, 35.46; H, 4.46. Found: C, 35.70; H, 4.82.

B. BASIC BERYLLIUM PROPIONATE

$$Be_4O(CH_3CH_2COO)_6$$

Twenty-five grams of basic beryllium carbonate is treated with 125 ml. of propionic acid in a 400-ml. beaker. When evolution of carbon dioxide has ceased, the solution is transferred to a porcelain evaporating dish and evaporated on a

---

* If the basic carbonate used does not react completely with acetic acid or if only beryllium oxide is available as starting material, conversion to freshly precipitated basic carbonate by the following procedure must precede treatment with acetic acid. Ten grams of beryllium oxide or 40 g. of the basic carbonate is dissolved in 50 ml. of concentrated sulfuric acid and the solution diluted to 500 ml. with distilled water. Aqueous ammonia (5N) is added until the solution is basic to litmus. The resulting suspension is clarified by digestion on the steam bath, and the precipitated hydroxide is removed by suction filtration and air-dried. The product is powdered in a mortar and suspended in 200 ml. of water containing 5 ml. of 5 N ammonia. The suspension is saturated with carbon dioxide either by addition of a few pieces of solid carbon dioxide or by bubbling in the gas. The container is stoppered and allowed to stand overnight. The resulting basic carbonate is removed by suction filtration and air-dried. It is then powdered and dried further in a desiccator.

† Calculation of percentage yield must be based upon the analytically determined beryllium content of the basic carbonate.

hot plate at 130 to 140°. When the cooler portions of the liquid begin to deposit crystals, the dish is allowed to cool. The solid cake of crude product is broken up and ground to a fine powder in a mortar. The powder is dissolved in 300 ml. of hot petroleum ether (b.p. 80 to 100°), and the filtered solution allowed to crystallize overnight in the refrigerator. The colorless crystals are removed by suction filtration and dried in the air. The yield is 45 g. (85 per cent, based on a starting material containing 15.4 per cent beryllium). The crystals melt at 137.5 to 138°, with preliminary softening at 134°. *Anal.* Calcd. for Be_4O-$(CH_3CH_2COO)_6$: C, 44.07; H, 6.17. Found: C, 44.18; H, 6.31.

4. STRONTIUM SULFIDE AND SELENIDE PHOSPHORS

SUBMITTED BY R. WARD,* R. K. OSTERHELD,* AND R. D. ROSENSTEIN*
CHECKED BY D. W. LYON† AND E. L. POOR†

The alkaline earth sulfides were among the earliest known synthetic phosphorescent materials. Recent work by Urbach[1] has shown that some of these substances exhibit the property of energy storage to a phenomenal degree and that this property may be developed by the addition of small quantities of two impurity cations or "activators." One of the activators serves to furnish electrons that may be promoted to higher energy states in the lattice by absorption of short-wave-length visible or ultraviolet light. This process is called "excitation." The other activator introduces potential wells in which some of the excited electrons are trapped. The potential barriers opposing the liberation of the electrons from these traps are high enough so that very few electrons are released by thermal energy at room temperature. Exposure to infrared radiation (about 1 μ), however, effectively releases the trapped electrons with

* Polytechnic Institute of Brooklyn, Brooklyn, N.Y.
† Chemical Division, Pigments Department, E. I. du Pont de Nemours and Company, Newport, Del.

consequent emission of visible light. This is known as "stimulation."

Several complementary pairs of activators have been used, but the most effective are those consisting of cerium-samarium and europium-samarium, the samarium ions furnishing the trapping centers. Phosphors of this type are best prepared from the pure alkaline earth sulfides or selenides by introducing the activators with the aid of a flux such as an alkaline earth halide or lithium fluoride.

Some of the procedures outlined below have been described previously.[2-5] They are designed for the preparation of phosphors that are to be used for quantitative studies of luminescence. Details are presented for the preparation of strontium nitrate, strontium chloride, strontium sulfate, and strontium selenite in a state of high purity; for the reduction of the sulfate to the sulfide and the selenite to the selenide; and for the conversion of the sulfide and the selenide into typical infrared-sensitive phosphors.

The necessity for unusual care in the preparation of reagents and the handling of all materials cannot be over-emphasized if reproducible results are to be obtained. While products having luminescent properties satisfactory for some practical uses can be obtained without recourse to the detailed procedures described here, such methods must be employed whenever reliable and reproducible materials are desired. For this reason, the preparation and purification of some of the reagents are first described along with several special techniques that have been found to be both useful and desirable.

Procedure

A. PREPARATION AND PURIFICATION OF REAGENTS

All glass and silica equipment employed should be cleaned with boiling nitric acid and washed with distilled water. Final washing should be made with twice distilled water.

The use of chromic acid cleaning solution must be avoided to prevent introduction of chromium. Flasks should be kept covered with inverted beakers to eliminate contamination from dust.

After the first step in the purification operations, any water that is used must be twice distilled, the second distillation being carried out in all-glass stills.

Where purified nitric acid is specified the purification is achieved by distilling reagent-grade nitric acid in a silica

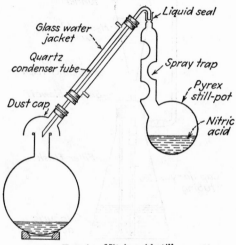

FIG. 1.   Nitric acid still.

still or in a glass still fitted with a silica condenser as shown in Fig. 1. The dust cap depicted in Fig. 1 may be made by appropriately cutting a round-bottomed flask.

The apparatus for preparing pure hydrochloric acid and for generating gaseous hydrogen chloride is shown in Fig. 2 (see also synthesis 34).

The ammonium hydroxide solution is prepared as needed by passing tank ammonia into doubly distilled water to saturation.

Selenium(IV) oxide is purified by three successive sublimations in the apparatus illustrated in Fig. 3[6] (see also synthesis 33). The sublimation chamber A is maintained at 250 to 300° and a slow stream of a dry mixture of oxygen and oxides of nitrogen is passed through the system to prevent decomposition and to sweep the vapors into the condenser B. The oxides of nitrogen are prepared by dropping a saturated solution of sodium nitrite into 6 N hydrochloric acid.

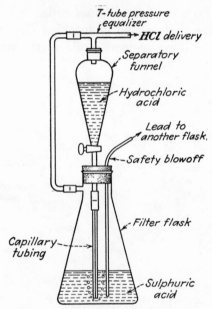

FIG. 2.   Hydrogen chloride generator.

Purified nitrogen is obtained by removing oxygen and water vapor from commercial tank nitrogen. This can be accomplished by passing the gases through a hot tube (375 to 400°) containing copper, and then through drying towers packed with barium oxide or phosphorus(V) oxide. An active form of copper especially satisfactory for removal of oxygen is obtained by reduction of the "wire form" of copper(II) oxide with hydrogen at about 360°.

Hydrogen sulfide is treated by bubbling the gas through a saturated barium hydroxide solution to remove other volatile acidic hydrides and then through glass wool to remove entrained material. An apparatus for treating solutions with hydrogen sulfide is shown in **Fig. 4.** When the gas is to be used to treat strontium sulfide it must be dried over phosphorus(V) oxide.

Ammonia is dried by passing the gas through towers

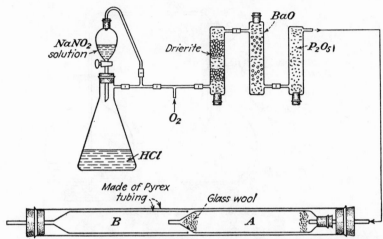

FIG. 3.   Apparatus for the purification of selenium(IV) oxide by sublimation.

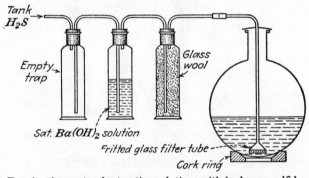

FIG. 4.   Apparatus for treating solutions with hydrogen sulfide.

filled with porous barium oxide.   Hydrogen is dried using phosphorus(V) oxide or barium oxide as the desiccant. Where a definite rate of gas flow is specified, the rate may be measured by means of a capillary manometer type of flowmeter, but there are other equally suitable types.

B. Special Techniques

A useful apparatus for filtering solutions is illustrated in Fig. 5. A mat of previously washed filter paper pulp deposited over the fritted-glass surface helps to retain finely

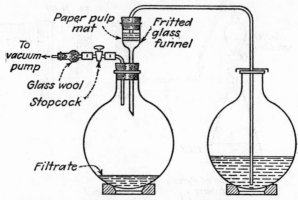

FIG. 5.   Filtering apparatus.

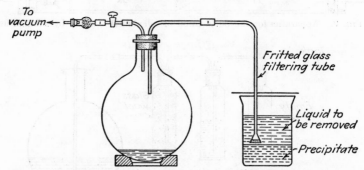

FIG. 6.   Apparatus for effecting the removal of liquid from a precipitate.

divided precipitates and makes the cleaning of the funnel easier as practically all of the precipitate is removed with the mat.   A flask other than the one intended as a receiver for the solution to be filtered is used to hold the funnel during the preparation and washing of the filter mat.

The "inverted filtration" technique employed to wash a precipitate is illustrated in Fig. 6. The liquid to be removed is drawn off through a sintered-glass dispersion disk. The disk is kept just above the surface of the settled precipitate until virtually all of the supernatant liquid has been removed. It is then pressed down into the precipitate to remove the remaining liquid. These procedures lessen considerably the danger of contamination from dust.

Figure 7 depicts three kinds of furnace-tube assemblies that are suitable for high-temperature, controlled-atmosphere operations: the assembly represented by (1) is satisfactory for use in a gas furnace; (2) and (3) can be employed

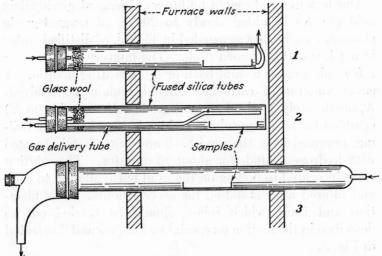

Fig. 7. Furnace-tube assemblies suitable for high temperature, controlled-atmosphere operations.

where either a gas or an electric tube furnace is available. Tubes (1) and (2) are conveniently removed from the furnace for rapid cooling. The extra opening in the adapter for tube (3) permits the insertion of a rake so that the boat may be moved in and out of the hot portion of the tube without admitting air.

C. PREPARATION OF STRONTIUM COMPOUNDS

Strontium Nitrate. In the procedure that follows, the concentration of barium ion is lessened by precipitation as the sulfate; ammonium oxalate is employed to reduce calcium-ion impurity. The heavy-metal contaminants are removed by precipitation with hydrogen sulfide. Bromine serves to oxidize iron(II) ion and to destroy any oxalate remaining in the solution, and nitric acid to oxidize sulfide ion. The strontium nitrate is finally purified by recrystallization. It should be noted that the solution is not filtered after each precipitation. The bulkier precipitates are left to carry down those substances which tend to be colloidal in nature.

One hundred sixty-eight milliliters of reagent-grade nitric acid (18 *N*) is added slowly to 200 g. of reagent-grade strontium carbonate suspended in 455 ml. of distilled water in a 1-l. round-bottomed flask. The mixture is heated for a few minutes on a sand bath or by a heating mantle. A small amount of carbonate should remain undissolved. Approximately 1 ml. of reagent-grade sulfuric acid (36 *N*) is added to the warm solution which is then heated to boiling, removed from the sand bath and immediately treated with hydrogen sulfide for about 15 minutes. The solution is again heated to boiling on the sand bath, allowed to cool, and filtered after standing for several hours. This filtration and those which follow should be carried out as described in the section on special techniques and illustrated in Fig. 5.

The pH of the solution is adjusted to 7* by addition of freshly prepared ammonium hydroxide solution. About 9 ml. of a saturated solution of reagent-grade ammonium oxalate is added, the solution is boiled, and, if necessary, the pH is again adjusted to 7. The hot solution is saturated with purified hydrogen sulfide, allowed to stand for several hours, and then filtered. By the addition of distilled nitric acid to the filtrate, the pH is lowered to 2, and 0.3 ml. of reagent-grade bromine is added to the solution, which is then boiled to remove excess bromine. The solution is just neutralized with freshly prepared ammonium hydroxide, treated with hydrogen sulfide while hot, and, after raising

* pH paper is used to determine pH throughout the preparation.

the pH to 8 with fresh ammonium hydroxide, is again treated with hydrogen sulfide for 15 minutes. The mixture is then boiled and filtered when the precipitate has settled. From 1 to 1.8 ml. of distilled nitric acid is next added to the filtrate to lower the pH to about 2; upon boiling the solution, a deposit of sulfur is obtained. After standing for several hours this is removed by filtration.

The resulting strontium nitrate solution is now concentrated by evaporation until bumping commences. It is cooled and nitric acid distilled into the solution until precipitation ceases. The supernatant liquid is removed as completely as possible, employing the technique shown in Fig. 6. The crystalline mass is dissolved in the smallest possible quantity of doubly distilled water and the solution is filtered. The crystallization procedure is repeated twice, yielding as the final product a saturated solution of thrice recrystallized strontium nitrate. This solution is diluted to 500 ml. with doubly distilled water and is used for the precipitation of strontium sulfate or strontium selenite.

Strontium Sulfate. The 500 ml. of strontium nitrate solution is heated to boiling in a round-bottomed flask and strontium sulfate is precipitated by the slow addition of a solution of 50 ml. of reagent-grade sulfuric acid (36 N) in 65 ml. of distilled water. When the precipitate has settled, the supernatant liquid is removed by the inverted filtration technique and the precipitate washed successively with five 200-ml. portions of hot, doubly distilled water. For the last washing the precipitate should be transferred to a beaker. It may then be removed more easily after drying for several hours at 200°. The strontium sulfate should not contain more than 20 parts per million of nitrate ion using diphenylamine–sulfuric acid reagent as a colorimetric test.[7] The yield is about 120 g.*

---

* The yield obtained depends primarily upon how much of the strontium nitrate is recovered in the three crystallizations. A considerably higher yield is possible, but if the degree of recovery becomes too high the quality of the product may suffer.

Strontium Sulfide. A weighed silica-glass boat is filled with the dry strontium sulfate and heated in a stream of sulfur dioxide and oxygen for 30 minutes at 980° using the assembly depicted in Fig. 7. The boat is then removed and weighed. It is replaced in the firing tube from which the air is swept by a stream of nitrogen. Dry hydrogen is then passed through the tube at about 200 ml. per minute while the charge is heated to 980° for 2 hours. The charge is cooled in an atmosphere of purified nitrogen. The weight loss should be close to the theoretical (34.84 per cent). The product is ground in a clean, dry, porcelain mortar in a dry box and returned to the silica-glass boat. It is then heated in a stream of purified hydrogen sulfide at 1000° for about 30 minutes, cooled in purified nitrogen and stored in a glass-stoppered bottle in a desiccator over barium oxide.

Strontium Selenite. A solution of 77 g. of sublimed selenium(IV) oxide in 154 ml. of distilled water is added to 500 ml. of pure strontium nitrate solution prepared as previously described. The solution is heated to boiling and fresh ammonium hydroxide solution is added until no further precipitation of strontium selenite occurs. The precipitate is drained and washed six times with 300-ml. portions of hot distilled water. The nitrate content should be less than 5 parts per million as determined by the diphenylamine–sulfuric acid test.[7] The strontium selenite is dried at 200° for several hours. The yield is about 125 g.

Strontium Selenide. The strontium selenite is heated in a weighed silica-glass boat in a stream of nitrogen at 835° for 30 minutes. The boat is then removed and weighed with its contents. It is replaced in the firing tube from which air has been swept by a stream of nitrogen. Dry ammonia gas is passed through the tube for 2 hours while the sample is held at 835°. The combustion-tube assembly designated as (3) in Fig. 7 is recommended for this operation as the adapter is particularly suited for leading off the excess ammonia and the gaseous selenium compounds that may be formed. The ammonia is swept out with nitrogen and the sample cooled in nitrogen.* The weight loss should be close to the theoretical (22.37 per cent). Examination under ultraviolet light of the sintered block of strontium selenide may reveal fluorescent areas where the selenite was in contact with the silica. These should be scraped off with a porcelain spatula and discarded. The remainder of the selenide should be stored in a glass-stoppered bottle in a desiccator over barium oxide.

Strontium Chloride. The purification of strontium chloride is carried out in a manner analogous to that used for strontium nitrate. A solution of the chloride is formed by dissolving 30 g. of reagent-grade strontium carbonate in 33.5 ml. of reagent grade 12 N hydrochloric acid and 20 ml. of distilled water. The quantities of reagents used in the purification of this solution are 0.14 ml. of reagent-grade sulfuric acid, 1.5 ml. of saturated ammonium oxalate solution, and about 0.2 ml. of bromine. Hydrochloric acid purified as specified in section A is used in place of the distilled nitric acid. The crystallization of strontium chloride 6-hydrate is accomplished by introducing gaseous hydrogen chloride just above the surface of the saturated solution. The thrice crystallized product is dried at 200° to give the anhydrous strontium chloride. The yield is about 15 g.†

D. Preparation of Infrared-sensitive Phosphors

Strontium Sulfide–Samarium–Europium Phosphor. To 3.0 g. of the pure strontium chloride, solutions of sama-

---

* Reduction with ammonia may cause the formation in the cooler portions of the tube of a black sublimate, which is highly sensitive to friction. In the early work, withdrawal of the boat containing the selenide resulted in explosions, which, in a few cases, shattered the combustion tube. To avoid difficulties from this source, it is advisable to clean out the cooler portions of the tube, prior to removal of the boat, with a glass-wool swab. Under no circumstances should this deposit be permitted to build up during successive runs. The nature of the explosive product has not been determined, but it is presumed to be a nitrogen selenide. The checkers minimized this hazard by lining the tube with paper before removing the boat.

† The yield depends greatly on the extent to which recovery is carried in the three crystallizations.

rium(III) and of europium(III) chlorides are added to give
0.4 mg. of samarium ion and 0.5 mg. of europium ion per
gram of strontium chloride. The water is removed by
evaporation and the mixture is dried at 200°. A mixture
of 25 g. of strontium sulfide and 2.5 g. of the strontium
chloride containing the activators is thoroughly ground in
a porcelain mortar in a dry box. The mixture is transferred
to a platinum boat and is heated in a stream of dry, purified
nitrogen for ½ hour at 1050°. Flow of nitrogen is continued until the product is cooled to room temperature.

The product is obtained as a buff-colored sintered block.
It is excited by exposure to ultraviolet light from a mercury
lamp, or to the blue light from a tungsten lamp from which
infrared light has been removed by suitable filters [such as
a 5 per cent copper(II) sulfate solution]. When the excit-
ing source of radiation is removed an orange phosphores-
cence may be observed lasting about a minute. Upon
exposure to infrared light, obtained by passing the light from
a tungsten lamp through a 2540 Corning filter, an instan-
taneous, bright, orange-colored emission will be obtained.

Strontium Selenide–Samarium–Europium Phosphor.
To 3 g. of pure strontium chloride, solutions of sama-
rium(III) and europium(III) chlorides are added to give
0.5 mg. of europium ion and 1.2 mg. of samarium ion per
gram of strontium chloride. The water is evaporated and
the mixture dried at 200°. Twenty-five grams of strontium
selenide and 2.5 g. of the strontium chloride containing the
activators are ground together in a porcelain mortar in a
dry box.* The mixture is heated in a platinum boat for
½ hour at 1050° in a stream of purified nitrogen and cooled
in the same nitrogen stream.

The sintered block should have a light yellow color. Its
excitation characteristics are the same as those of the corresponding sulfide phosphor, but the emission color is a
yellowish-green.

---

* A more sensitive phosphor may be obtained by incorporating into the
mixture 1 g. of calcium sulfide.

Strontium Sulfide–Samarium–Cerium Phosphor. Samarium and cerium(III) chloride solutions are added to 3 g. of purified strontium chloride to give a flux containing 0.2 mg. of samarium ion and 1.0 mg. of cerium ion per gram of strontium chloride. The water is evaporated and the flux is dried at 200°. Twenty-five grams of strontium sulfide and 2.5 g. of the strontium chloride containing the activators are ground together in a porcelain mortar in a dry box. The mixture is heated in a platinum boat at 1050° in a stream of purified nitrogen for ½ hour and is cooled in the same nitrogen stream.

This phosphor block has a pistachio-green color. It is best excited with ultraviolet light or by long exposure to radium emission. The color of the light emitted on stimulation of the excited phosphor with infrared light is blue-green.

General Properties

The luminescent properties of these phosphors are destroyed by grinding but are restored on heating in an inert atmosphere above 600°. In the powder form they are very susceptible to hydrolysis and oxidation on exposure to moist air and should therefore be stored in tightly sealed containers. The powders may be molded into appropriate shapes which will be retained on heating to 1000°. An active powder form of these phosphors can be made by heating an intimate mixture consisting of 50 weight per cent of reagent grade magnesium oxide (predried by heating to 1000°) with 50 per cent of the finely ground phosphor powder.

References

1. URBACH, PEARLMAN, and HEMMENDINGER: *J. Optical Soc. Am.*, **36**, 372 (1946).
2. SMITH, ROSENSTEIN, and WARD: *J. Am. Chem. Soc.*, **69**, 1725 (1947).
3. STRIPP and WARD: *ibid.*, **70**, 401 (1948).
4. RUSSO: thesis, Polytechnic Institute of Brooklyn, 1946.
5. FONDA and SEITZ: "Preparation and Characteristics of Solid Luminescent Materials," John Wiley & Sons, Inc., New York, 1948.
6. PITHA: *J. Chem. Education*, **23**, 403 (1946).

7. FEIGL: "Qualitative Analysis by Spot Tests," 3d ed., p. 244, Elsevier Publishing Company, New York, 1946.

5. BARIUM THIOCYANATE

$$Ba(OH)_2 + 2NH_4SCN \rightarrow Ba(SCN)_2 + 2NH_3 + 2H_2O$$

SUBMITTED BY KARL M. HERSTEIN*
CHECKED BY R. H. TENNYSON† AND G. L. EICHHORN†

Barium thiocyanate was first prepared by Berzelius, who roasted barium hexacyanoferrate(II) with sulfur.[1] It has also been obtained by reaction of barium carbonate with a solution of thiocyanic acid,[2] by conversion of ammonium thiocyanate through the copper(I) thiocyanate by consecutive reactions with copper(I) chloride and barium hydroxide,[3] by treatment of Prussian blue with barium sulfide,[4] and by reaction of barium sulfide, sulfur, and cyanamide.[5] The procedure described below makes possible the preparation of barium thiocyanate in any desired quantity from barium hydroxide and ammonium thiocyanate as starting materials. The 3-hydrate,[6-8] which is obtained first, is dehydrated readily to yield anhydrous barium thiocyanate.

Procedure

Seventy-six grams (1 mol) of ammonium thiocyanate and 158 g. (0.5 mol) of $Ba(OH)_2 \cdot 8H_2O$ are placed in a 500-ml. round-bottomed flask and shaken until the mass liquefies. The solution is boiled until ammonia is no longer evolved, the evaporated water being replaced at intervals. The mixture must now be alkaline to phenolphthalein. If necessary, more barium hydroxide is added, and the process repeated. At this point the solution usually contains a precipitate, which may range from white to dark gray in color. The solution is filtered through a sintered-glass Büchner funnel; if such a funnel is not available, the filter

* Herstein Laboratories, Inc., New York, N.Y.
† University of Illinois, Urbana, Ill.

paper must be precoated with just enough kieselguhr, Celite 521, or Filter-Cel, to form a continuous mat.* To the filtrate is added 6 N sulfuric acid until the solution is only faintly alkaline to litmus (just colorless to phenolphthalein); the remainder of the barium hydroxide is neutralized with carbon dioxide. The solution is heated to boiling to remove any barium hydrogen carbonate that may have formed. It is preferable, but not absolutely necessary, to digest the mixture overnight on a steam bath. The solution is filtered through paper precoated as before, the filtrate is heated to boiling, 0.5 g. of activated charcoal is added, and the solution is filtered again.

The final filtrate is concentrated until the boiling point rises to 125°, but no higher. The solution is allowed to cool to room temperature and is then placed in an ice bath. The crystals of the 3-hydrate that form are collected on a Büchner funnel.† The product is dried in air. Yield, approximately 115 g. (75 per cent). *Anal.* Calcd. for $Ba(SCN)_2$: SCN, 45.76. Found: SCN, 46.04.

Properties

Barium thiocyanate is a white solid that is very soluble in water but has a very steep temperature-solubility gradient. This solid is also soluble in acetone, methanol, ethanol, methylamine and ethylamine, moderately soluble in isopropylamine and dimethylamine, but insoluble in trimethylamine.[6] The anhydrous salt is very hygroscopic. Crystallization from water yields the 3-hydrate as well-formed, needle-shaped crystals. Double salts are formed with the thiocyanates of the alkali and other alkaline earth metals.[8]

---

* If larger quantities than those specified are to be prepared, a glass filter cloth is very convenient.

† The filtrate may be concentrated further to effect some increase in yield. (If larger quantities are to be prepared, the recovery process can be repeated several times and the yield increased accordingly. For preparations on the scale described here, however, more than one such repetition is not worth the time involved.)

The reaction mixture used in this procedure may find application in freezing mixtures because of its high negative heat of reaction. Barium thiocyanate has been used in the dye and color printing industries and as a dispersing agent for cellulose. It can be converted readily by treatment with a dilute sulfuric acid to give dilute solutions of thiocyanic acid, or into the thiocyanates of other metals by precipitation of barium sulfate.

References

1. GMELIN: "Handbuch der anorganischen Chemie," 8th ed., No. 30, p. 329, Verlag Chemie, G.m.b.H., Berlin, 1931.
2. MEITZENDORFF: *Pogg. Ann.*, **56**, 68 (1842).
3. STORCK and STROBEL: *Dinglers Polytech. J.*, **235**, 157 (1880).
4. HÖLBLING: *Z. angew. Chem.*, **10**, 297–8 (1897).
5. Hene: German patent 517759 (1928); *cf. Chem. Abstracts*, **25**, 2818 (1931).
6. TCHERNIAC: *Ber.*, **25**, 2627 (1892).
7. OCCLESHAW: *J. Chem. Soc.*, **1931**, 57.
8. FOOTE and HICKEY: *J. Am. Chem. Soc.*, **59**, 649 (1937).

CHAPTER III

6. BORON CHLORIDE AND BROMIDE

$$BF_3 + AlX_3 \rightarrow AlF_3 + BX_3 \ (X = Cl \text{ or } Br)$$
$$KBF_4 + AlX_3 \rightarrow AlF_3 + BX_3 + KF$$

SUBMITTED BY E. LEE GAMBLE*
CHECKED BY HAROLD S. BOOTH† AND HAROLD HALBEDEL†

Large quantities of boron chloride are best prepared by the chlorination of a mixture of boron oxide (or borax) and carbon.[1] Smaller amounts may be obtained (1) by the chlorination of amorphous boron[2] or metallic borides[3] or (2) by the reaction between boron oxide and phosphorus(V) chloride in a sealed tube.[4] A more convenient laboratory method for the preparation of boron chloride makes use of the reaction between boron fluoride and aluminum chloride.[5] For the preparation of boron bromide, the reaction of boron fluoride and aluminum bromide is recommended as much less troublesome than other methods. Potassium tetrafluoborate[6,7] may be used in place of the boron fluoride in each of these syntheses.

Procedure

Apparatus. The reaction is carried out most conveniently in an all-glass apparatus constructed as shown in Fig. 8. A 1-l. round-bottomed flask is sealed to the bottom of a 500-ml. distilling flask by means of a 25-cm. length of 30-mm. tubing. The tube for the introduction of the boron fluoride passes through a one-hole cork stopper in the distilling flask and extends to the middle of the larger flask. The smaller flask serves as a condenser to prevent

* Massachusetts Institute of Technology, Cambridge, Mass.
† Western Reserve University, Cleveland, Ohio.

large quantities of aluminum chloride from subliming with the product. Attached to the arm of the distillation flask is a U-tube cooled with solid carbon dioxide and alcohol and protected by a drying tube.

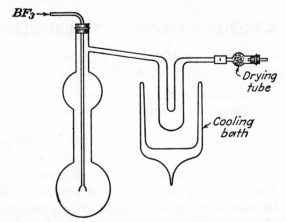

FIG. 8. Apparatus for the preparation of boron chloride.

Boron Chloride. Sixty-seven grams (0.5 mol) of anhydrous aluminum chloride is placed in the reaction flask. A boron fluoride generator[7] [containing sufficient quantities of materials to generate 132 g. (2 mols) of boron fluoride]* is connected to the reaction flask by means of a small bubbler containing sulfuric acid. The rate of flow of the boron fluoride should be fairly rapid, about 30 minutes being required for passage of 2 mols of gas. After the apparatus has been swept out with boron fluoride, the large flask containing the aluminum chloride is heated gently by means of a free flame. With rise in temperature the reaction soon starts. Heating is continued as long as reaction takes place. Both flasks are then heated strongly by using two burners, in order to remove the product from the reaction mixture. The stream of boron fluoride continues to pass through the reaction flasks until the boron chloride

* Cylinders of boron fluoride are available commercially; their use eliminates the necessity of employing a laboratory generator.

has been distilled. After removal of the product and continued heating, the aluminum fluoride falls from the sides of the flask as a light white powder.

The product collects in the U-tube, which is sealed off after completion of the reaction and its contents distilled through a good column. The yield is 47 g. (80 per cent).

Boron Bromide. One hundred thirty-three and one-half grams of aluminum bromide (0.5 mol) (synthesis 7) is distilled into the reaction flask and treated with boron fluoride as described for boron chloride. It is desirable to reflux the aluminum bromide gently in the stream of boron fluoride. The contents of the flask soon solidify. When this happens the mass is heated strongly in boron fluoride to distill all of the product over into the U-tube where it is condensed. Small amounts of bromine* in the product are readily removed by shaking with mercury. Yield, 87.7 g. (70 per cent). This product is satisfactory for most purposes, but may be redistilled through a good column to effect further purification.

Modification. One hundred thirty-three grams (1 mol) of aluminum chloride (or 267 g. of aluminum bromide) and 62 g. (0.5 mol) of potassium tetrafluoborate are placed in the apparatus described above (or in an ordinary distilling flask) and heated by means of an oil bath for 4 hours, with the temperature slowly increasing from 150 to 175°. The product is condensed by liquid nitrogen and then fractionated. Yield: BCl_3, 30 g. (0.26 mol) (52 per cent based on KBF_4); BBr_3, 37.6 g. (30 per cent).

Properties

Boron chloride and bromide melt at $-107°$ and $-46°$, respectively, to give colorless liquids of high refractive index and large coefficients of thermal expansion. Boron chloride boils at 12.5° and the bromide, at 90.8°. At 0° the

---

* The amount of free bromine in the product may also be reduced by adding a few grams of granular aluminum to the aluminum bromide in the reaction flask.

specific gravity of the chloride is 1.434; of the bromide, 2.650.

The halides of boron are readily hydrolyzed by the moisture in air. They react with a wide variety of electron-pair donors to form coordination complexes of the type $R_3N:BX_3$. In general, the halogens are not progressively replaced by other groups to form mixed halides except by means of the Grignard reagent.

References

1. WEBER and GUYER: U.S. patent 2097482; *cf. Chem. Abstracts*, **32**, 316 (1938).
2. MOISSAN: *Ann. chim. phys.*, [7] **6**, 312 (1895).
3. MAZZETTI and DE CARLI: *Atti accad. naz. Lincei*, [31] **II**, 119 (1922).
4. GUSTAVSON: *Z. Chem.*, **6**, 521 (1870); *Jahresber. Chem.*, **23**, 285 (1870).
5. GAMBLE, GILMONT, and STIFF: *J. Am. Chem. Soc.*, **62**, 1257 (1940).
6. VAN DER MEULEN and VAN MATER: INORGANIC SYNTHESES, **1**, 24 (1939).
7. BOOTH and WILLSON: *ibid.*, **1**, 21 (1939).

7. ALUMINUM BROMIDE

$$2Al + 3Br_2 \rightarrow 2AlBr_3$$

SUBMITTED BY DOUGLAS G. NICHOLSON,* PAUL K. WINTER,† AND HERBERT FINEBERG‡
CHECKED BY J. R. MILLS§ AND L. F. AUDRIETH§

Aluminum bromide has been finding increasing application as an acid catalyst in organic synthesis; it has recently become of industrial importance in the alkylation of aromatic hydrocarbons with ethylene,[1] and in the isomerization of normal hydrocarbons.[2-4] It is also used in the polymerization of olefins,[5] and to some extent in the Friedel-Crafts reaction.[6] It has been found particularly useful in such reactions since it is not only more soluble in organic media, but also more active catalytically than aluminum chloride.

Winter and Cramer[8] have described a procedure for pre-

* University of Pittsburgh, Pittsburgh, Pa.
† General Motors Corporation, Detroit, Mich.
‡ General Chemical Company, New Haven, Conn.
§ University of Illinois, Urbana Ill.

paring this material in relatively large quantities. This method has been modified to make it suitable for the preparation of laboratory quantities either in bulk (procedure A), in small individual samples (procedure B), or as a high-purity material (procedure C).

Procedure A

A diagram of the apparatus used for the preparation of aluminum bromide in larger amounts is shown in Fig. 9. The reaction vessel A consists of a 250-ml. distilling flask

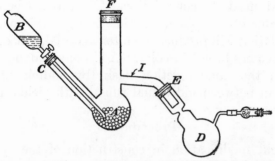

FIG. 9.   Apparatus for the preparation of aluminum bromide in larger quantities.

to which is sealed a short, wide-diameter (about 12-mm. i.d.) side tube. The bromine delivery tube B leading from the separatory funnel (bromine reservoir) is sealed to C by means of a mixture of asbestos and sodium silicate. E and F are rubber stoppers covered with aluminum foil. A calcium chloride tube is attached to the receiving flask D.

Sixty grams of bromine, dried over concentrated sulfuric acid, is placed in B. The bottom area of the reaction flask A is covered with a thin layer of dry glass wool. Sufficient granular aluminum (30-mesh), dried in an oven at 110° for several hours, is placed in the reaction flask to fill the latter almost to the mouth of the exit tube leading to the receiver D.* The dry reaction flask containing the granular alumi-

* Aluminum bromide liquid and vapor thus come in contact with excess aluminum, which serves to remove dissolved bromine.

num is then heated to approximately 100° with an open flame, the flame removed, and the bromine allowed to come in contact (drop-by-drop addition) with the aluminum metal. Initially, and occasionally throughout a run, the aluminum powder glows with some sparking and flashing. The reaction flask is shaken occasionally and the aluminum–aluminum bromide mixture broken up with a glass rod to prevent channeling.

After the entire amount of bromine has been added (about ½ to 2 hours), the aluminum bromide is distilled from the reaction flask into the receiver, which may then be sealed off at the constriction. The product is obtained as a light brown solid. Yield, 56.1 g. (85 per cent). Redistillation will produce a whiter material, but on standing it becomes brown in color. Additional batches may be made in the same reaction flask (by adding additional aluminum between individual runs), with yields up to 98 per cent.

Procedure B

A slight modification in construction of the apparatus described under procedure A will permit the preparation of small individually sealed samples of aluminum bromide instead of one large sample of the product. The delivery tube I, Fig. 10, leading from the reaction flask A, Fig. 9, is sealed to a ground-glass* joint D (standard taper 19/33). The outer section of this joint is attached to a length of glass tubing F of the same diameter as I. A calcium chloride tube attached at G protects the open end of the apparatus from atmospheric moisture. Several small ampoules, 4 to 6 mm. i.d. (or larger as desired), are sealed in a spiral about the tube F and at right angles to it. The tube F is attached in the position shown in Fig. 10, so that when the product is distilled, the uppermost tube will collect the first portion. When the ampoule is one-third to one-half filled, the

* In order to avoid contamination, grease or lubricant materials should not be used in the ground-glass joint.

receiver tube F is rotated at the joint D until the second ampoule bulb is in position to receive a second portion of the product. This rotation procedure may be continued until all the ampoules contain the desired amounts of aluminum bromide. The ampoules are then sealed off (removed) from the larger tube and the product is available for use when desired.

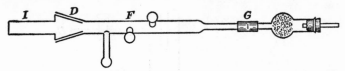

FIG. 10.   Attachment for collecting small samples of aluminum bromide.

Procedure C

A third procedure which is adaptable to the preparation of material of high purity, either in bulk or in small samples, makes use of an all-glass setup in which precautions are observed to prevent hydrolysis and contamination. If desired, a considerable amount of aluminum bromide may be prepared at one time and stored in the reaction flask. Small samples of aluminum bromide may then be obtained by distillation from the initial aluminum–aluminum bromide mixture.

One hundred grams of aluminum turnings, or wire, degreased by treatment with carbon tetrachloride, trichloroethylene, or other organic solvent, and dried at 110°, is placed in the reaction flask A, Fig. 11. (Note that a small amount of glass wool is placed about the bromine delivery tube opening to prevent plugging.) The condenser B, receiver C, and bromine reservoir F are attached. A stream of commercial nitrogen, dried over phosphorus(V) oxide in a drying line provided with a mercury safety well, is used to flush out moist air. This dry nitrogen enters through E_1, and leaves through either E_2 or E_3. After flushing, the nitrogen stream is maintained across the head, entering the receiver through E_3 and leaving it through

the condenser at E_2 throughout the reaction.   One hundred
twenty-five milliliters of bromine is placed in the reservoir
F.   The bromine is added at such a rate that the heat of
reaction causes the aluminum bromide formed to reflux
about midway up the air condenser.   After all the bromine
has been added, a considerable excess of aluminum should
remain.   External heat is then applied to maintain the

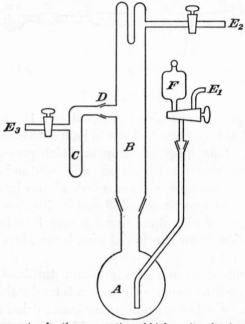

Fig. 11.   Apparatus for the preparation of high-purity aluminum bromide.

reflux until the liquid returning down the condenser walls
is colorless.   The presence of an excess of aluminum and
the continuation of the refluxing are necessary, since bromine is extremely soluble in liquid aluminum bromide and
cannot be separated successfully by distillation.   If any
unreacted bromine remains, the liquid will be yellow to
brownish-red in color.   If desired, the aluminum bromide
may be cooled, and, after cooling, the nitrogen inlet E_3 and
outlet E_2 closed.   The product will remain in good condition indefinitely in such storage.

To withdraw samples, the stream of dry nitrogen is caused to flow across the head from E_2 to exit from the receiver at E_3. A drying tube containing phosphorus(V) oxide is attached at E_3 as a further precaution against entrance of moisture. The bromide is then distilled into the receiver. The first small sample may be discolored and, if so, should be discarded. In order to replace the receiver, dry nitrogen is first passed from E_1, to both E_2 and E_3, so that when the receiver C is detached, dry nitrogen flows out of both the receiver connection D and the head. A new receiver is placed in position at once, and the old receiver, emptied or stoppered as desired.

If necessary, more aluminum may be added to flask A, Fig. 11, by raising the condenser and further amounts of product prepared without dismantling and cleaning the apparatus.

Properties

Aluminum bromide melts at 97°; numerous values for the boiling point within the range 250 to 270° have been reported. The specific gravity is 3.205_4^{18} for the solid. It fumes vigorously in moist air and must therefore be stored or used under anhydrous conditions. It is quite soluble in a variety of organic solvents, such as benzene, toluene, nitrobenzene, ethylene bromide, carbon disulfide, and simple hydrocarbons.[3] Aluminum bromide has been reported to form a series of stable compounds with ammonia containing 1, 3, 5, 6, 7, 9, and 14 mols of ammonia per mol of aluminum bromide. In all likelihood these are really mixtures of NH_4Br and its ammoniates with ammonobasic salts of $AlBr_3$ or $AlN·xNH_3$. The compounds $AlBr_3·H_2S$, $AlBr_3·\frac{1}{2}SO_2$, and $AlBr_3·PH_3$ as well as numerous addition compounds with organic substances have also been reported.

The disposal of anhydrous aluminum bromide is best accomplished by melting and pouring slowly into running water. The hydration is very violent and may destroy the container if water is added directly in any considerable amount.

References

1. BURK and HUGHES: U.S. patent 2399662 (May 7, 1946); cf. Chem. Abstracts, **40**, 4876 (1946).
2. BLANDING: U.S. patent 2383586 (August 28, 1945); cf. Chem. Abstracts, **40**, 711 (1946).
3. GRUMMITT, SENSEL, SMITH, BURK, and LANKELMA: J. Am. Chem. Soc., **67**, 910 (1945).
4. BISHOP, BURK, and LANKELMA: J. Am. Chem. Soc., **67**, 914 (1945).
5. SPARKS and THOMAS: U.S. patent 2389693; cf. Chem. Abstracts, **40**, 2030 (1946).
6. ADAMS: "Organic Reactions," Vol. 3, pp. 1–82, John Wiley & Sons, Inc., New York, 1946.
7. THOMAS: "Anhydrous Aluminum Chloride in Organic Chemistry," Am. Chem. Soc. Monograph 87, p. 875, Reinhold Publishing Corporation, New York, 1941.
8. WINTER and CRAMER: Ind. Eng. Chem., **32**, 856 (1940).

CHAPTER IV

8. CARBON TETRAIODIDE

$$CCl_4 + 4C_2H_5I \xrightarrow{AlCl_3} CI_4 + 4C_2H_5Cl$$

SUBMITTED BY R. E. McARTHUR* AND J. H. SIMONS*
CHECKED BY KARL M. BECK†

Carbon tetraiodide has been prepared by the interaction
of carbon tetrachloride and various metallic iodides, such
as aluminum iodide,[1] boron iodide,[2] calcium iodide,[1,3] and
lithium iodide.[3] The procedure here described makes use
of readily available materials and involves the reaction of
carbon tetrachloride with ethyl iodide in the presence of
aluminum chloride.[4]

Procedure

A 200-ml. flask is fitted with a cork stopper containing a
calcium chloride drying tube to permit the evolution of
ethyl chloride but to prevent the influx of moisture from

* Pennsylvania State College, State College, Pa.
† University of Illinois, Urbana, Ill.

the air. Into the flask is weighed 6 g. (0.039 mol) of dry carbon tetrachloride, 24 g. (0.154 mol) of dry ethyl iodide, and 1 g. (0.0075 mol) of anhydrous aluminum chloride.* The flask is quickly closed with the stopper and drying tube, since traces of moisture render the catalyst ineffective. Both carbon tetrachloride and ethyl iodide must be dried over anhydrous calcium sulfate and redistilled before use.

Immediately on adding the catalyst the reaction mixture turns red and ebullition and effervescence begin. Red crystals form gradually on the bottom of the flask. Occasional swirling helps to keep the reactants well mixed. After about 45 minutes a heavy deposit of red crystals will have formed; very little liquid will be present. The crystals are collected in a Büchner funnel using mild suction, and are washed with three 25-ml. portions of ice-cold water to remove the aluminum chloride and then with three 25-ml. portions of ethyl alcohol to remove unreacted carbon tetrachloride and ethyl iodide. Washing with water causes the crystals to darken, but subsequent treatment with the alcohol restores the product to its natural bright red color. The crystals are dried in a vacuum desiccator containing sulfuric acid. The yield is about 12 g. (60 per cent).

Properties

Carbon tetraiodide is a bright red crystalline material, possessing an odor like that of iodine. The density at 20° is 4.32 g./ml. Both heat and sunlight cause decomposition to iodine and tetraiodoethylene.[5] The compound is insoluble in water and in alcohol, but hydrolyzes slowly in contact with cold water to produce iodoform and iodine; it is decomposed by hot alcohol. Carbon tetraiodide is soluble in benzene. At 100° it reacts with hydrogen to form iodoform; at still higher temperatures this reaction yields methylene iodide and methyl iodide.[3]

* This represents a mol ratio of $1CCl_4:4C_2H_5I:0.2AlCl_3$. The quantities can be scaled up to molar amounts if more product is desired.

References

1. GUSTAVSON: *Ann.*, **172**, 173 (1874).
2. MOISSAN: *Compt. rend.*, **113**, 19 (1891).
3. LANTENOIS: *ibid.*, **156**, 1385 (1913).
4. WALKER: *J. Chem. Soc.*, **85**, 1090 (1904).
5. MOISSAN: *Bull. soc. chim.*, [3] **7**, 746 (1892).

9. CYANAMIDE

$$2CaCN_2 + 2H_2O \rightarrow Ca(HCN_2)_2 + Ca(OH)_2$$
$$Ca(HCN_2)_2 + H_2SO_4 \rightarrow 2H_2NCN + CaSO_4$$

SUBMITTED BY L. A. PINCK* AND J. M. SALISBURY†
CHECKED BY H. A. DEWALT, JR.,‡ A. B. HERRICK,‡ AND E. B. MOHR‡

Cyanamide, H_2NCN, has been prepared by (1) desulfurizing thiourea with mercury(II) oxide,[1,6] lead acetate,[2] or bromine,[3] (2) passing gaseous cyanogen chloride into ammonia dissolved in anhydrous ether,[4] and (3) oxidizing thiourea with alkaline permanganate.[5] The method described below is an adaptation for laboratory use of a commercial procedure[8] that uses calcium cyanamide as a starting material.

Procedure

A. AQUEOUS SOLUTION OF CYANAMIDE

A slurry made by mixing 600 g. of crude calcium cyanamide containing 62.3 per cent calcium cyanamide§ with 600 ml. of water‖ is poured into a 10-in. Büchner funnel.¶

* U.S. Department of Agriculture, Bureau of Plant Industry, Soils and Agricultural Engineering, Beltsville, Md.
† American Cyanamid Company, Stamford Laboratories, Stamford, Conn.
‡ University of Illinois, Urbana, Ill.
§ Aero Cyanamid, Minimum Hydrate, contains 60 to 63 per cent calcium cyanamide but on storage in a humid atmosphere the calcium cyanamide content will decrease. Samples containing as low as 56.9 per cent calcium cyanamide have been used successfully.
‖ In order to obtain the most efficient extraction, it is necessary to have the crude calcium cyanamide finely ground so that 65 per cent will pass through a 200-mesh sieve.
¶ The best results are obtained with a filter cake approximately ½ in. thick.

The outlet of the funnel is connected to a glass spiral condenser, which leads into a filter flask connected to a water pump. Ice water is circulated through the jacket of the condenser to cool the filtrate. The filter cake is extracted with 3.6 l. of water at 60° at such a rate that there is generally only a thin aqueous layer above the cake. The extraction requires about 25 minutes.* The hot water is allowed to remain in contact with the slurry for only a very short time; the resultant solution of calcium hydrogen cyanamide must be cooled immediately to below 20°. Approximately 3.8 kg. of filtrate† is obtained. The filtrate is immediately cooled to 10° and then treated with 20 per cent aqueous sulfuric acid to precipitate the calcium and to lower the pH to 5.1.‡ Approximately 1 kg. of acid will be needed.

The mixture is filtered. Using specified quantities, the filtrate will weigh about 4.1 kg., and will contain about 80 per cent of the cyanamide present in the original calcium cyanamide as a 3.5 per cent solution.

The filtrate may be concentrated with respect to cyanamide by vacuum distillation§ at 40 mm. through a 12-in.

* This operation should be done as quickly as possible, but some lag must be allowed to give time for the water to extract the cyanamide. The recommended leaching system is one in which advantage is taken of the higher rate of solution and hydrolysis of calcium cyanamide in hot water, at the same time avoiding the formation of dicyanodiamide in objectionable amounts.

† Analysis of the filtrate from a typical preparation showed 2.81 per cent cyanamide nitrogen, indicating that 89.2 per cent of the original cyanamide had been extracted.

‡ The pH of the free cyanamide solution should be kept at about 5.0. Previous work at the Stamford Research Laboratories of the American Cyanamid Company, indicates that at a pH of 6 or higher free cyanamide may polymerize violently to dicyanodiamide during the concentration. At a pH of about 3, cyanamide decomposes to urea.

§ The solution must be stirred during concentration to expedite removal of water and to prevent bumping. A simple and convenient stirring device that will operate efficiently for use in systems under reduced pressure is depicted in Fig. 12. A piece of rubber tubing A serves as the seal between the shaft of the stirrer B and the glass bearing guide C. A few drops of glycerol are applied at B to lubricate the glass-rubber interface and to permit column 1 in. o.d. packed with ⅛-in. Raschig rings to remove the water. There is a strong tendency for the cyanamide to be carried over into the distillate, and it is therefore necessary to use a column to minimize such losses. Distillation should be carried out behind a safety screen. Aqueous solutions of cyanamide of any desired concentration up to 20 to 25 per cent can be prepared easily in this manner. Such solutions are often employed for synthetic purposes (syntheses 10 and 11) rather than the solid material.

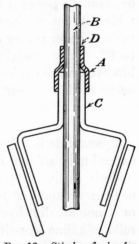

FIG. 12. Stirring device for operation under reduced pressure.

B. CRYSTALLINE CYANAMIDE

If crystalline cyanamide is desired, the concentration of the solution prepared in A is continued until the temperature in the pot reaches 70°.*

The warm solution is filtered to remove the small amount of calcium sulfate that crystallizes during the evaporation. The filtrate is then cooled to 10° to effect crystallization of cyanamide which is separated by filtration and dried in an evacuated desiccator over phosphorus(V) oxide. The crystalline mass should be broken up at intervals in order to

---

easy rotation. The tube C is conveniently sealed to a male taper joint and can thus be fitted readily to the all-glass distillation apparatus recommended for the concentration operation.

* Toward the end of the concentration process, the pot temperature will rise rapidly from approximately 40 to 70°. A good yield of cyanamide can be obtained if a pressure no higher than 10 mm. and a maximum temperature of 40° are employed, but poor yields are obtained if distillation is attempted at 40 mm. at this same temperature, simply because insufficient water is thus removed. The temperature of the residue in the flask should be kept as low as possible to minimize formation of dicyanodiamide and should never exceed 70°. Evaporation of cyanamide solutions to dryness is hazardous due to the tendency of cyanamide to polymerize with explosive violence when heated in the presence of too little water.

facilitate complete desiccation. The yields of cyanamide, with a purity of 93.5 per cent as determined by analysis, will vary between 110 and 130 g. and average about 120 g. or about 65 per cent of theory based on the calcium cyanamide content of the starting material. Additional cyanamide of lesser purity can be obtained by cooling the filtrate to 0°. It is inadvisable to effect further concentration, however, since explosive polymerizations are very prone to occur at this concentration.

Properties

Cyanamide is a crystalline solid melting at 46°C. and is exceedingly soluble in water, alcohol, and ether. Cyanamide is easily recrystallized from a solution of two parts of benzene and one part of ether. In the presence of acid or strong alkali it hydrolyzes readily to urea, whereas under mild alkaline conditions it polymerizes exothermally to dicyanodiamide (synthesis 10). Cyanamide combines with hydrogen chloride[9] to form a dihydrochloride and forms salts with metals.[7,10] It reacts with hydrogen sulfide[11] or mercaptans[12] to form thiourea or substituted isothioureas and reacts with alcohols[13] in the presence of acid to form substituted isoureas. With formaldehyde[14] cyanamide forms methylol compounds; with amines[15] it forms substituted guanidines. Cyanamide can be acylated with acylating agents,[10,16] or alkylated with alkylating agents.[10] When fused with potassium hydroxide,[17] cyanamide forms potassium cyanate. When treated with hydrazine salts,[18] it forms aminoguanidonium salts. Cyanamide is toxic to the skin and readily attacks iron, steel, copper, lead, and, to a slight extent, Duriron. Glass and enamelware are found to be most resistant.[19]

References

1. VOLHARD: *J. prakt. Chem.*, [2] **9**, 6 (1874).
2. WALTHER: *J. prakt. Chem.*, [2] **54**, 510 (1896).
3. RATHKE: *Ber.*, **12**, 776 (1879).
4. CLOËZ and CANNIZZARO: *Compt. rend.*, **32**, 62 (1851).

5. WERNER: *J. Chem. Soc.*, **115**, 1168 (1919).
6. HANTZSCH and WOLVEKAMP: *Ann.*, **331**, 282 (1904).
7. FRANKLIN: "The Nitrogen System of Compounds," A.C.S. Monograph, pp. 93–97, Reinhold Publishing Corporation, New York, 1935.
8. HETHERINGTON and PINCK: U.S. patent 1673820 (1928); *cf. Chem. Abstracts*, **22**, 2816 (1928).
9. PINCK and HETHERINGTON: *Ind. Eng. Chem.*, **18**, 629 (1926).
10. DRECHSEL: *J. prakt. Chem.*, [2] **11**, 284 (1875).
11. HEUSER: U.S. patent 1991852 (1935); *cf. Chem. Abstracts*, **29**, 2180 (1935).
12. ARNDT: *Ber.*, **54**, 2236 (1921).
13. STIEGLITZ and McKEE: *Ber.* **33**, 1517 (1900).
14. GRIFFITH: U.S. patent 2019490 (1935); *cf. Chem. Abstracts*, **30**, 538 (1936).
15. BISCHOFF: *J. Biol. Chem.*, **80**, 345 (1928).
16. MERTENS: *J. prakt. Chem.*, [2] **17**, 1 (1878).
17. EMICH: *Monatsh.*, **10**, 321 (1889).
18. FANTL and SILBERMANN: *Ann.*, **467**, 274 (1928).
19. Unpublished work of the U.S. Department of Agriculture.

10. DICYANODIAMIDE

(Cyanoguanidine)

$$2H_2NCN \rightarrow H_2NC(\!\!=\!\!NH)NHCN$$

SUBMITTED BY L. A. PINCK*
CHECKED BY R. L. PHELPS†

Methods for preparation of dicyanodiamide involve polymerization of cyanamide under controlled conditions in aqueous solutions in the presence of metallic hydroxides or ammonia.[1] Dicyanodiamide is an important chemical intermediate and is used for the preparation of guanidonium nitrate,[2] biguanide,[3] and numerous other derivatives of the ammonocarbonic acids.[4] The present method is easily adaptable to preparation of laboratory quantities.

Procedure

A neutral aqueous solution of cyanamide (synthesis 9), or a solution made very slightly alkaline with ammonia, is

* U.S. Department of Agriculture, Bureau of Plant Industry, Soils and Agricultural Engineering, Beltsville, Md.
† American Cyanamid Company, Stamford, Conn.

concentrated by evaporation under reduced pressure at a temperature of 40° or less until the residual solution contains approximately 20 to 25 per cent cyanamide.

One kilogram of the concentrated solution is transferred to an evaporating dish and while still warm (about 40°) is treated with 70 to 80 g. of concentrated aqueous ammonia to bring the concentration of the latter to about 2 per cent.* The temperature of the solution is then raised as rapidly as possible on a steam bath. Heating is continued for 15 to 20 minutes until the cyanamide has been converted completely into dicyanodiamide, as shown by the nonformation of the characteristic yellow precipitate of silver cyanamide when an ammoniacal silver nitrate solution is added to a test portion.[5] The solution is cooled and the solid product separated by filtration and dried at 100°. In a typical experiment there was obtained from 1 kg. of a 25 per cent solution 260 g. of dicyanodiamide (m.p. 206 to 208°) containing 0.46 per cent water by analysis. The yield is practically quantitative.

Properties

Dicyanodiamide melts at 209.5° (corr.) and can be crystallized in the form of rhombic plates from water, alcohol, or a mixture of the two. It is only slightly soluble in water, moderately soluble in alcohol and in liquid ammonia. Aqueous solutions are neutral, but liquid ammonia solutions are acidic in character, and react with metallic oxides and amides to form well-defined salts.[6]

References

1. PINCK and HETHERINGTON: *Ind. Eng. Chem.*, **27**, 834 (1935); GRUBE and NITSCHE: *Z. angew. Chem.* **27**, 368 (1914).
2. SMITH: INORGANIC SYNTHESES, **1**, 96 (1939).
3. DAVIS: *J. Am. Chem. Soc.*, **43**, 2234 (1921).
4. FRANKLIN: "Nitrogen System of Compounds," chaps. X and XI, Reinhold Publishing Corporation, New York, 1935.

* Maximum conversion of cyanamide is achieved in solutions containing at least 20 per cent H_2NCN and 2 per cent NH_3.

5. PINCK: *Ind. Eng. Chem.*, **17**, 459 (1925).
6. FRANKLIN: *J. Am. Chem. Soc.*, **44**, 501 (1922).

11. AMINOGUANIDONIUM HYDROGEN CARBONATE

(Aminoguanidine Bicarbonate)

$$2N_2H_4 \cdot H_2SO_4 + 2NaOH$$
$$\rightarrow (N_2H_4)_2 \cdot H_2SO_4 + Na_2SO_4 + 2H_2O$$
$$(N_2H_4)_2 \cdot H_2SO_4 + 2H_2NCN$$
$$\rightarrow [C(NH_2)_2(N_2H_3)]_2SO_4$$
$$[C(NH_2)_2(N_2H_3)]_2SO_4 + 2KHCO_3$$
$$\rightarrow 2[C(NH_2)_2(N_2H_3)]HCO_3 + K_2SO_4$$

SUBMITTED BY J. T. THURSTON* AND L. P. FERRIS, II*
CHECKED BY H. A. DeWALT, JR.† AND A. B. HERRICK†

Aminoguanidonium salts have been prepared by chemical,[1] catalytic,[2] and electrolytic[3] reduction of nitroguanidine. Nitrosoguanidine has also been reduced chemically[4] and catalytically[5] to aminoguanidonium salts. Hydrazinolysis of nitrosoguanidine[4] and of *S*-alkylisothiourea sulfates[6] has yielded aminoguanidine; the direct preparation of aminoguanidonium hydrogen carbonate from aqueous cyanamide, hydrazine, and carbon dioxide has been described.[7,8] The present procedure is a modification of a method devised by Fantl and Silbermann,[9] who allowed disodium cyanamide to react with hydrazonium hydrogen sulfate in aqueous solution, after neutralizing with sulfuric acid, and subsequently isolated aminoguanidine as the hydrogen carbonate by addition of potassium hydrogen carbonate.

Procedure

Into a 1-l., three-necked, round-bottomed flask equipped with a mechanical stirrer, thermometer, and addition

* American Cyanamid Company, Stamford, Conn.
† University of Illinois, Urbana, Ill.

funnel are placed 87 g. (0.67 mol) of hydrazonium hydrogen sulfate and 515 ml. of water. After stirring a short time, 27 g. (0.67 mol) of 98 per cent solid sodium hydroxide is added. As soon as complete solution is achieved, the pH is determined and adjusted to a value within the range 5.0 to 6.0. The stirred solution is cooled in an ice bath and maintained below 10° while 160 g. (1.0 mol) of 26 per cent aqueous cyanamide solution (synthesis 9) is added in about 10 minutes. The flask is removed from the ice bath and the addition funnel replaced by a reflux condenser; the solution is allowed to stand for 2 hours, during which time it will have warmed to room temperature. The stirred solution is then warmed on a steam bath (solution temperature 89 to 92°) for 3 hours and allowed to cool overnight. After filtration to remove any extraneous materials, 100 g. (1.0 mol) of solid potassium hydrogen carbonate is added to the filtrate, which is stirred vigorously until the salt has dissolved. The solution is surrounded by an ice bath; precipitation of aminoguanidonium hydrogen carbonate begins within 15 to 30 minutes. After standing in the ice bath for a total of 2 hours, the colorless solid is removed by filtration, washed well with cold water to remove soluble inorganic salts, and air-dried. It is well to allow the filtrate to stand in the ice bath for an additional period, as occasionally a second crop of product of equal purity is obtained. The yield varies from 80 to 83 g. (88 to 90 per cent). Decomposition occurs in a preheated oil bath at 171 to 173°. The compound is 96 per cent pure by nitrite titration.

Analysis

Kjeldahl determinations give only half of the total nitrogen present in aminoguanidonium hydrogen carbonate, but the Dumas method will give satisfactory results. The method employed for determining the purity of aminoguanidonium hydrogen carbonate is based on a sodium nitrite procedure devised by the Remington Arms Company.

A 2.2687-g. sample of aminoguanidonium hydrogen carbonate is weighed into a 250-ml. beaker. Thirty milliliters of distilled water is added, followed by 30 ml. of HCl (diluted 1:3). The solution is titrated with standard 1.0 N sodium nitrite using starch-KI test paper as an outside indicator. After 20 ml. of the sodium nitrite has been added, a 20-ml. portion of the solution is removed and set aside; the addition of sodium nitrite solution is continued in $\frac{1}{2}$-ml. portions and a test made with starch-KI paper after each addition. When the end point has been reached, the portion that was withheld is returned by washing all of the solution into the beaker; the titration is continued cautiously until the first blue tinge is observed on the test paper.

Per cent purity $= 3 \times$ milliliters nitrite $\times$ normality
nitrite solution

Properties

Aminoguanidonium hydrogen carbonate is a colorless, odorless solid, whose solubility is less than 0.5 g./100 ml. of water at room temperature. The pH of a saturated aqueous solution is 7.5 to 8.0. It cannot be recrystallized from hot water because of its instability. It decomposes slowly above 50° both as a solid and in solution, and melts with decomposition at 171 to 173° in a preheated oil bath. A comprehensive review of the chemistry of aminoguanidine has been written by Lieber and Smith.[10]

References

1. THIELE: *Ann.*, **270**, 1 (1892).
2. LIEBER and SMITH: *J. Am. Chem. Soc.*, **58**, 2170 (1936).
3. SHREVE and CARTER: *Ind. Eng. Chem.*, **36**, 423 (1944).
4. THIELE: *Ann.*, **273**, 133 (1893).
5. LIEBER and SMITH: *J. Am. Chem. Soc.*, **59**, 1834 (1937).
6. HEYN: French patent 618064; *cf. Chem. Zentr.*, II, 503 (1927).
7. ZIEKE: German patent 689191; *cf. Chem. Abstracts*, **35**, 3650 (1941).
8. ZIEKE and HOFFMANN: German patent 730331; *cf. Chem. Abstracts*, **38**, 378 (1942).
9. FANTL and SILBERMANN: *Ann.*, **467**, 274 (1928).
10. LIEBER and SMITH: *Chem. Revs.*, **25**, 213 (1939).

12. AMMONIUM DITHIOCARBAMATE

$$2NH_3 + CS_2 \rightarrow NH_2CSSNH_4$$

SUBMITTED BY ROGER A. MATHES*
CHECKED BY H. S. BOOTH† AND R. D. KIRK†

Ammonium dithiocarbamate has been prepared by using the following organic solvents as diluents for the reaction between carbon disulfide and ammonia: esters;[1] alcohol;[2] ether and alcohol;[3] ketones;[4] ethers;[5] nitriles;[6] and nitro compounds.[7] Isopropyl acetate is employed in the procedure that follows.

Procedure

A 5-l. three-necked flask is fitted with a mechanical stirrer, a vent tube or reflux condenser, a thermometer, and an ammonia inlet tube.‡ Two liters of isopropyl acetate§ and 304 g. (4 mols) of carbon disulfide are added to the tared reaction flask. It is cooled to about 20° and ammonia is bubbled in with vigorous stirring. The rate of ammonia flow is carefully adjusted so that only a small excess passes out of the vent tube. A temperature of 20 to 30° is main-

* B. F. Goodrich Co., Research Center, Brecksville, Ohio.
† Western Reserve University, Cleveland, Ohio.
‡ The ammonia inlet tube should be at least 8 mm. i.d. When a tube of smaller diameter or a gas distribution tube is used, the flow of ammonia may be obstructed due to crystallization of the product.
§ The presence of even a small amount of water (either in the ester or when introduced from commercial ammonia) causes side reactions to take place that greatly reduce the purity of the product. Commercial isopropyl acetate is usually sufficiently dry. If necessary, this solvent can be dried conveniently by stirring vigorously with 200 ml. of 50 per cent sodium hydroxide solution for 10 min. Dry ammonia can be obtained by using the following procedure: Approximately 500 ml. of commercial liquid ammonia is run into a 1-l. unsilvered Dewar flask. Metallic sodium is added in small pieces until a permanent dark blue color appears, then another small piece in excess. The flask is now closed with a one-hole rubber stopper from which a glass outlet tube and rubber tubing are led, first through a trap, and then to the ammonia inlet tube of the reaction flask. A steady flow of gaseous ammonia at the rate desired can now be obtained by placing an infrared bulb near the Dewar and regulating the distance of the bulb from the flask.

tained during the reaction. Ammonium dithiocarbamate precipitates as a light yellow, crystalline product.

The progress of the reaction can be followed by occasionally weighing the complete equipment and noting the weight increase. If the proper ammonia addition rate is maintained so that carbon disulfide and isopropyl acetate are not carried out of the vent tube, the final weight increase will amount to approximately 136 g. (8 mols). About 2 hours are required to add all the ammonia. Stirring is continued for 15 minutes after the ammonia addition has been completed. The slurry of ammonium dithiocarbamate is filtered on a Büchner funnel and is washed with petroleum ether or hexane to facilitate drying. The product is dried as rapidly as possible at room temperature by stirring with a porcelain spatula. The dry weight is 405 to 422 g. (92 to 96 per cent yield) of a product of high purity (95 per cent or higher).

For the preparation of an aqueous solution of ammonium dithiocarbamate, 500 ml. of water is added to the reaction flask containing the slurry in isopropyl acetate. The mixture is agitated for a few minutes and the light yellow water solution of ammonium dithiocarbamate (lower layer) is separated from isopropyl acetate. The yield can be determined quite accurately by noting the increase in weight of the measured volume of water added.

Analysis

Dilute copper(II) sulfate solution gives a yellow flocculent precipitate when added to a dilute solution of ammonium dithiocarbamate. If a dilute solution of dithiocarbamate is heated to accelerate its decomposition, the resulting thiocyanate ion can be detected with iron(III) chloride.

A good quantitative method for the determination of dithiocarbamate involves its precipitation as the sparingly soluble zinc salt. The precipitate is then dried at about 60° and weighed. An alternative procedure involves ignition to zinc oxide. Miller[3] used a volumetric method involving a titration with iron(III) chloride in the presence of a definite excess of hydrochloric acid. In this method dithiocarbamic acid is quantitatively oxidized to thiuram disulfide.

Properties

Ammonium dithiocarbamate is an unstable, light yellow, crystalline solid. The melting point is not a suitable criterion for estimating the purity of ammonium dithiocarbamate because it melts with decomposition. The products of decomposition are ammonium thiocyanate, sulfur, and hydrogen sulfide. The dry product can be preserved for several days at 0° with little decomposition. Under the same conditions, a water solution is stable for several weeks.

Ammonium dithiocarbamate is useful in the synthesis of heterocyclic compounds, particularly mercaptothiazoles.

References

1. MATHES: U.S. patent 2117619 (May 17, 1938); *cf. Chem. Abstracts*, **32,** 5002 (1938).
2. *a.* ZIESE: *J. Chem. Phys.*, **41,** 172 (1824).
   b. DEBUS: *Ann.*, **73,** 26 (1850).
   c. MULDER: *ibid.*, **168,** 232 (1873).
   d. FREUND and BACHRACH: *ibid.*, **285,** 201 (1895).
   e. DELEPINE: *Bull. soc. chim.*, [4] **3,** 643 (1908).
   f. LEVI: *Gazz. chim. ital.*, **61,** 673 (1931).
3. *a.* MILLER: *Contribs. Boyce Thompson Inst.*, **5,** 31 (1933).
   b. JULIAN and STURGIS: *J. Am. Chem. Soc.*, **57,** 1126 (1935).
4. MATHES: U.S. patent 2123370; *cf. Chem. Abstracts*, **32,** 6672 (1938).
5. MATHES: U.S. patent 21223371; *cf. ibid.*
6. MATHES: U.S. patent 2123373; *cf. ibid.*
7. MATHES: U.S. patents 2123372 and 2207627; *cf. Chem. Abstracts*, **34,** 7934 (1940).

13. ORGANOSILICON COMPOUNDS

BY EUGENE G. ROCHOW*

A great many organosilicon† compounds are known,[2] and they have been shown to vary widely in their physical properties and chemical behavior. Certain similarities and

* Harvard University, Cambridge, Mass.
† As in other phases of the chemistry of organometallic substances, it is

differences between related compounds of silicon and carbon,[2] silicon and boron,[3] and silicon, tin, and lead[4] have been pointed out, but in general there has been little success in explaining the chemistry of silicon wholly in terms of the chemistry of its congeners. Few elements show more individuality of chemical behavior.

The general characteristics of organosilicon substances are (1) wide variation of reactivity in the carbon-silicon bond, depending upon the substituents on both atoms; (2) comparatively easy removal of halogens and acid radicals from the silicon by hydrolysis, but rather difficult removal from the carbon except in some favorable structures;[5] and (3) a decided tendency to form polymeric structures containing alternate silicon and oxygen (or nitrogen or sulfur) atoms. This behavior indicates that silicon is quite electropositive with respect to bonded carbon,[6] and sufficiently positive with respect to oxygen to make the siloxane bond about half ionic in character.[6,7]

Synthesis[1,8]

The classical methods for preparing alkyl and aryl derivatives of silicon include:

1. The Action of Alkyls of Mercury or Zinc on Silicon Halides or Esters:

$$(C_6H_5)_2Hg + SiCl_4 \rightarrow (C_6H_5)_2SiCl_2 + HgCl_2$$

Such reactions usually are carried out without solvents, using zinc compounds to supply alkyl groups and mercury compounds to supply aryl groups.

2. The Action of Sodium on Mixtures of Silicon Halides with Hydrocarbon Halides (Wurtz Condensation):

$$4C_6H_5Cl + SiCl_4 + 8Na \rightarrow (C_6H_5)_4Si + 8NaCl$$

customary to limit the term organosilicon to those derivatives of the metallic element which have one or more carbon-silicon bonds. (Metallic carbides constitute a special case and are considered separately.) Consequently, in this brief discussion the many other types of organic derivatives in which organic groups are linked to silicon through oxygen, sulfur, nitrogen, etc., will not be considered.

This method is particularly well suited to the preparation of silicon tetraalkyls, because the heat of reaction at the surface of the sodium usually forces the reaction to completion. A two-stage Wurtz reaction allows partial substitution.[20]

3. The Action of Grignard Reagents on Silicon Halides or Esters:

$$2C_2H_5MgCl + SiCl_4$$
$$\rightarrow (C_2H_5)_2SiCl_2 + 2MgCl_2$$
$$2CH_3MgBr + Si(OC_2H_5)_4$$
$$\rightarrow (CH_3)_2Si(OC_2H_5)_2 + 2Mg(OC_2H_5)Br$$

The preparation of organochlorosilanes by this method requires that the Grignard reagent be added slowly and with stirring to silicon tetrachloride, which then undergoes a series of consecutive competitive reactions[21] to replace the chlorine atoms successively with organic groups. A mixture of substitution products is always obtained, from which the desired compounds must be isolated by distillation.

To these there have now been added some newer methods which offer particular advantages:

4. The Direct Reaction of Hydrocarbon Halides with Elementary Silicon:

$$2CH_3Cl + Si \xrightarrow{Cu} (CH_3)_2SiCl_2$$

This is a general reaction, usually carried out by passing the vapor of the hydrocarbon halide through heated silicon powder. Most alkyl chlorides react at 250 to 325° when copper, as a catalyst, is intimately mixed with the silicon;[22] without the catalyst, higher temperatures are required, and there is extensive pyrolysis of the organic groups. Chlorobenzene reacts with silicon at 400 to 440°, with silver as catalyst. The method is best suited to the preparation of dialkyl- and diaryldihalogenosilanes, but if organotrichlorosilanes are desired, a mixture of hydrogen chloride and alkyl chloride may be employed as reactant.

5. The Reaction of Hydrocarbons with Silicon Halides by Passing the Mixed Vapors Through a Heated Tube.[1]

6. The Reaction of Lithium Alkyls with Silicon Halides and Hydrides,[1] in the Manner of the Grignard Reactions.
7. The Reaction of Alkenes and Alkynes with Silicon Hydrides.[11,12,23]

$$CH_2{=}CHC_6H_{13} + HSiCl_3 \xrightarrow{\text{peroxides}} C_8H_{17}SiCl_3$$

This is an addition of Si–H groups to double or triple bonds, and may be catalyzed by dissolved organic peroxides or by exposure to ultraviolet light. Acetylene adds one equivalent of trichlorosilane to form vinyltrichlorosilane, which then may add another equivalent of the silane.

These methods embrace a wide variety of laboratory techniques, for 1 and 2 may be carried out in sealed tubes, 2, 3, 6, and 7 may be carried out in solution, 4 and 5 may be heterogeneous gas-phase reactions at elevated temperature, and 7 may involve reactions in pressure vessels above the critical temperatures of the reactants. Hence it becomes impossible to state which method is best suited for the preparation of a desired compound; much will depend upon the available equipment and the experimenter's familiarity with the different techniques. In general, the Grignard method is the most flexible and can be used for the introduction of one to four groups on silicon with yields up to 70 per cent, using any group capable of forming a Grignard reagent. The Wurtz method is still convenient at times, especially for preparing completely substituted compounds. Method 4 is best used for synthesizing dialkyldihalogenosilanes, particularly with small alkyl groups, with which yields up to 70 per cent are obtainable. Method 6 is adapted to the attachment of large alkyl groups like *tert*-butyl,[9,10] and method 7 provides an easy way to make alkyltrichlorosilanes from a wide variety of olefins.[11,12]

The more complex organosilicon compounds usually are derived from organohalogenosilanes as intermediates. Silanols may be made by hydrolyzing the corresponding halogenosilanes, and organosiloxanes result from the dehydration of silanols. Silylamines and silazanes result from the action of ammonia on halogenosilanes. Further reactions of the organic groups often are possible after the carbon-silicon bonds are established.

Properties

Extensive tables of the known organosilicon compounds and their properties are given in references 1 and 8. Since most organosilicon syntheses begin with the preparation of halogenosilanes or alkoxysilanes, the properties of these are of particular interest. Almost all are colorless liquids that are sufficiently volatile to be purified by distillation, and all are subject to hydrolysis. The boiling points of most homologous series change regularly with composition, as in the phenylchlorosilanes:

TABLE I

Compound	Boiling Point, 760 mm.
$SiCl_4$	57.6°
$C_6H_5SiCl_3$	201.5
$(C_6H_5)_2SiCl_2$	305.2
$(C_6H_5)_3SiCl$	378
$(C_6H_5)_4Si$	428

However, in some series a distinct maximum boiling point is reached:

TABLE II

Compound	Boiling Point
$SiCl_4$	57.6°
CH_3SiCl_3	65.7
$(CH_3)_2SiCl_2$	70.0
$(CH_3)_3SiCl$	57.3
$(CH_3)_4Si$	26.5

The boiling points of the methylbromosilanes change regularly with composition, as do those of the ethylchlorosilanes, but the ethylbromosilanes again reach a maximum boiling point. It follows that in the preparation of new compounds the expected boiling points should not be inferred by interpolation. The calculation of boiling points by the use of boiling-point numbers[24] is much more reliable.

Uses. Compounds of silicon with one, two, or three methyl groups and a complement of hydrolyzable atoms or groups are used to prepare the structural units of polymethylpolysiloxanes[13] for silicone oil and rubber. Methylchlorosilanes also are used to provide water-repellent films on glass and cellulose,[14] and a variety of other organosilicon compounds may be similarly employed. Chlorosilanes and ethoxysilanes with alkyl and aryl groups that are particularly heat-stable and resistant to oxidation are hydrolyzed to polysiloxane ("silicone") resins for insulation and protective coatings.[15,16] Organosilicon polymers also find use as foam suppressors in lubricating oils and as mold-release agents, two applications that depend in part on immiscibility with hydrocarbons of high molecular weight.

Nomenclature. Rules for naming organosilicon compounds have been adopted and published by Crane.[17] The recommended names are based on the terms "silane" and "disilane" for SiH_4 and Si_2H_6, "disiloxane" for $H_3SiOSiH_3$, and "disilazane" for $H_3SiNHSiH_3$; organosilicon compounds are named as derivatives of these according to established rules of order and numbering. Older literature will be found to follow widely divergent "systems," and hence the abstracts are scattered under many index names. The older reviews[18,19] are often helpful when abstracts fail.

References

1. BURKHARD, ROCHOW, BOOTH, and HARTT: *Chem. Revs.*, **41**, 97 (1947). Tables of all the known compounds and their properties are given, and the bibliography is complete to June 3, 1946.
2. BYGDÉN: "Silizium als Vertreter des Kohlenstoffs organischer Verbindungen," inaugural dissertation, Upsala, 1916.
3. STOCK: "Hydrides of Boron and Silicon," Cornell University Press, Ithaca, N.Y., 1933.
4. BEHAGHEL and SEIBERT: *Ber.*, **66**, 922 (1933); GIACOMELLO, *Gazz. chim. ital.*, **68**, 422 (1938).
5. SOMMER and WHITMORE: *J. Am. Chem. Soc.*, **68**, 485 (1946).
6. WRIGHT and HUNTER: *ibid.*, **69**, 803 (1947).
7. ROTH: *ibid.*, **69**, 474 (1947).
8. ROCHOW: "Chemistry of the Silicones," John Wiley & Sons, Inc., New York, 1946.

9. GILMAN and CLARK: *J. Am. Chem. Soc.*, **69**, 967 (1947).
10. TYLER, SOMMER, and WHITMORE: *ibid.*, **69**, 981 (1947).
11. SOMMER, PIETRUSZA, and WHITMORE: *ibid.*, **69**, 188 (1947).
12. BURKHARD and KRIEBLE: *ibid.*, **69**, 2687 (1947).
13. ROCHOW: *Trans. Electrochem. Soc.*, **90**, 249 (1946).
14. NORTON: *Gen. Elec. Rev.*, **47** (8), 6 (1944).
15. KILBORNE: *Machine Design*, **18**, (8), 100 (1946).
16. PATTERSON: *Official Digest Federation Paint & Varnish Production Clubs*, July and October, 1946, March, 1947.
17. CRANE: *Chem. Eng. News*, **24**, 1233 (1946).
18. GODDARD and GODDARD: "Friends' Textbook of Inorganic Chemistry," Vol. 11, Part 1, pp. 248–291, Charles Griffin & Co. Ltd., London, 1928.
19. KRAUSE and VON GROSSE: "Die Chemie der metallorganischen Verbindungen," pp. 254–295, Verlagsbuchhandlung Gebrüder Borntraeger, Berlin, 1937.
20. SCHUMB and SAFFER: *J. Am. Chem. Soc.*, **63**, 93 (1941).
21. FROSS: *ibid.*, **65**, 2406 (1943).
22. HURD and ROCHOW: *ibid.*, **67**, 1057 (1945).
23. SOMMER, PIETRUSZA, and WHITMORE: *ibid.*, **70**, 484 (1948).
24. LEWIS and LEWKIRK: *ibid.*, **69**, 701 (1947).

14. DIMETHYLDICHLOROSILANE

(Dimethylsilicon Dichloride)

$$2CH_3Cl + Si \xrightarrow{Cu} (CH_3)_2SiCl_2$$

SUBMITTED BY EUGENE G. ROCHOW*
CHECKED BY WILLIAM S. TATLOCK†

Dimethyldichlorosilane may be prepared by the Grignard reaction, but the sluggishness of the reaction of methyl chloride with magnesium and the low solubility of methylmagnesium chloride in ether make the preparation more difficult. The use of methyl bromide facilitates the reaction with magnesium but results in some undesired halogen exchange with silicon tetrachloride in the second stage.[1]

The recommended method involves the direct reaction of methyl chloride with silicon at 300° in the presence of copper as a catalyst.[2] The copper is deposited on powdered silicon by the reduction of copper(I) chloride, a procedure

* Research Laboratories, General Electric Company, Schenectady, N.Y.
† Harvard University, Cambridge, Mass.

that is not necessarily the most efficient but is quite easily carried out.*

Procedure

One hundred seventy grams of commercial silicon† (crushed to pass an 80-mesh sieve) is ground in a mortar with 30 g. of copper(I) chloride.‡ The ground powders (or pressed lumps) are packed loosely into a pyrex tube 3 cm. in diameter and 40 cm. long which is drawn down at one end and sealed to a water condenser. The other end is closed by a stopper bearing a short inlet tube and a thermometer with its bulb imbedded in the charge. The condenser is connected to a closed receiver which leads through a trap held at −80° to a drying tube. The reaction tube is heated in an ordinary combustion furnace while a slow stream of methyl chloride (7 g./hr.) is passed through the charge directly from a cylinder. When the temperature§ reaches about 265°, a reaction takes place to form silicon tetrachloride; copper will deposit on the silicon. The temperature is adjusted to 300 to 305° and the gas flow continued for 70 hours or more.

The contents of the trap and the receiver are then mixed and allowed to warm slowly; some unreacted methyl chloride evaporates and leaves a mixture containing methylchlorosilanes, corresponding to a yield of approximately 90 per cent based on the methyl chloride that has undergone reaction. This mixture is distilled at a high reflux ratio in a column of high efficiency, yielding the following fractions in approximately the proportions shown in the following table.

* The yield of dimethyldichlorosilane by the reaction here shown depends considerably upon the method of incorporating the copper with the silicon. Highest yields are obtained from a reactive mass made by pressing together copper and silicon powders and firing the pellets in hydrogen.[5]

† Approximately 97 per cent silicon, from Electro Metallurgical Co., Niagara Falls, N.Y.

‡ The grinding may be omitted if a press is available; the mixed powders are pressed in the form of a disk or block, which is then broken into ½-inch lumps.

§ The temperature at which this reaction takes place may be somewhat higher, and the reaction may start with difficulty. Once begun, however, it is extremely vigorous and exothermal.

Products	Boiling points	Percentage by weight	
CH_3SiHCl_2............	41°	11	(11.7)†
$(CH_3)_3SiCl + SiCl_4$...	54–58°	9*	(23.2)
CH_3SiCl_3............	65.7°	35	(27.8)
$(CH_3)_2SiCl_2$.........	70.0°	40	(28.1)
Residue.............	Above 70°	5	(4.7)

* $SiCl_4$ boils at 57.6°, $(CH_3)_3SiCl$ at 57.3°, and an azeotrope of the two at 54.5°.
† Figures in parentheses represent yields obtained in a typical check run. Some 4.5 per cent $SiHCl_3$ was also recovered. (W.S.T.)

The products may be analyzed by hydrolyzing in a mixture of ice and ether and titrating liberated hydrochloric acid with standard base.

Properties

Dimethyldichlorosilane is a colorless liquid that freezes at −76.1°, boils at 70.0°, and has a density of 1.06 g./ml. at 25°. It hydrolyzes readily in moist air and reacts with water to form a mixture of polymeric dimethylsiloxanes ("methyl silicone") containing products possessing both cyclic and linear structures.[3,4]

References

1. KRAUSE and VON GROSSE: "Die Chemie der metallorganischen Verbindungen," p. 259, Borntraeger, Berlin, 1937; photolithographed by Edwards Bros., Inc., Ann Arbor, Mich., 1943.
2. ROCHOW: *J. Am. Chem. Soc.*, **67**, 963 (1945).
3. HUNTER, HYDE, WARRICK, and FLETCHER: *J. Am. Chem. Soc.*, **68**, 667 (1946).
4. PATNODE and WILCOCK: *J. Am. Chem. Soc.*, **68**, 358 (1946).
5. PATNODE: U.S. patent 2380997: *cf. Chem. Abstracts*, **39**, 5058 (1945).

15. VINYLCHLOROSILANES

$$C_2H_5SiCl_3 + SO_2Cl_2 \rightarrow ClC_2H_4SiCl_3 + SO_2 + HCl$$
$$ClC_2H_4SiCl_3 + C_9H_7N \rightarrow CH_2{=}CHSiCl_3 + C_9H_7N \cdot HCl$$

SUBMITTED BY DALLAS T. HURD*
CHECKED BY E. G. ROCHOW† AND W. S. TATLOCK†

Vinyl silicon compounds have been prepared by the direct reaction of vinyl chloride with elemental silicon[1] and by

* Research Laboratory, General Electric Company, Schenectady, N.Y.
† Harvard University, Cambridge, Mass.

the dehydrochlorination of triethyl(chloroethyl)silane with aqueous caustic.[2] The yields of vinylchlorosilanes from the first reaction generally are not high, and the second reaction is not suitable for use with chlorosilanes.

Vinylchlorosilanes are prepared most conveniently from ethylchlorosilanes by a modification of the chlorination-dehydrochlorination reactions in which the dehydrohalogenation is effected by a high-boiling tertiary amine. Although the experimental procedure herein described is based on the preparation of vinyltrichlorosilane, the method can be adapted to the synthesis of many other vinyl silicon compounds.

Procedure

(Caution: *This reaction must be done in a hood!*)

Sixteen hundred grams of ethyltrichlorosilane* (10 mols) is placed in a 3-l. round-bottomed flask together with 1400 g. of freshly distilled sulfuryl chloride.† The flask is fitted with a large-capacity, water-cooled reflux condenser‡ and heated on a hot plate or burner until the refluxing vapors have swept the air from the flask and are condensing up in the column of the condenser. At this point about 4 g. of benzoyl peroxide is added through the top of the condenser. Owing to the low boiling point of the mixture, activation of the reaction proceeds very slowly at first, but as the evolution of gas continues and the amount of chlorinated product increases, the boiling point rises. This increases the rate of

---

* Ethylchlorosilanes may be prepared either by the direct reaction of ethyl chloride with silicon-copper[3] or by the reaction of silicon tetrachloride with an ethyl Grignard reagent.[4]

† The chlorination reaction with sulfuryl chloride is very sensitive to traces of oxygen or free chlorine, and may at times be difficult to start. The commercial product was found to work well if it was freshly distilled just before using. Material standing for a day or two exposed to light and air was not satisfactory without redistillation.

‡ A good hood is a prime necessity for the chlorination reaction as large volumes of sulfur dioxide and hydrogen chloride are evolved. This also requires a reflux condenser of considerable capacity if loss of material is to be avoided.

activation and care must be taken that the reaction does not get out of control. Toward the later stages of the reaction the boiling point rises quite sharply and increased heat will have to be supplied to keep the mixture boiling. When this occurs an additional 2 g. of peroxide is added gradually until the reaction is complete and the flow of hydrogen chloride and sulfur dioxide from the top of the condenser has ceased.

The flask is allowed to cool and the liquid product is distilled.* This comprises small amounts of sulfuryl chloride and unreacted ethyltrichlorosilane, together with the (α- and β-chloroethyl) trichlorosilanes. Negligible amounts of the higher chlorinated products are found. The major reaction product is (β-chloroethyl) trichlorosilane, b.p. 153 to 154°. Smaller amounts of the α-isomer boiling at 138° are isolated. The total yield of (chloroethyl) trichlorosilanes (α and β) is about 1400 g. or 70 per cent of theory.

One liter of dry, freshly distilled quinoline[2]† (about 30 mol per cent in excess) is placed in a 3-l. distilling flask and to it 1160 g. (6 mols) of (chloroethyl) trichlorosilane is added slowly with continual agitation. Heat is evolved and a solid addition product settles out. The flask is transferred to a hot plate and is fitted with a water-cooled condenser on the outlet tube. A thermometer is inserted through a cork in the neck of the flask which is then surrounded with an asbestos shield. Heat is applied slowly to the flask and the contents are brought to the boiling point. The dehydrochlorination reaction proceeds smoothly but maximum yield of vinyltrichlorosilane is obtained only by careful control of the temperature during the dehydrochlorination

---

* Satisfactory separations of unreacted ethyltrichlorosilane from the (α- and β-chloroethyl) trichlorosilanes may be obtained by careful distillation from a modified Claisen flask. (W.S.T.)

† Synthetic quinoline (Eastman Kodak Company—White Label) acts satisfactorily without distillation. (W.S.T.) Other tertiary amines, e.g., pyridine and lutidine, may be used for the dehydrohalogenation reaction if quinoline is not available.

reaction. The reading on the thermometer in the neck of the flask should be kept between 100 and 110°. The reaction products distill over and are collected in a clean bottle. When the reaction is complete, the temperature of the liquid refluxing in the neck of the flask rises rapidly to over 200°.*

Redistillation† of the reaction product yields vinyltrichlorosilane (b.p. 92°) together with a small amount of silicon tetrachloride. A yield of 560 g. is obtainable corresponding to 60 per cent of theory.

In similar fashion, vinylmethyldichlorosilane may be prepared from ethylmethyldichlorosilane (35 per cent yield), and divinyldichlorosilane can be synthesized from diethyldichlorosilane with somewhat smaller yields. Ethyltrimethylsilane may in like manner be converted to vinyltrimethylsilane.

Properties

Vinyltrichlorosilane is a colorless, corrosive liquid boiling at 92°. Its specific gravity is 1.264 (27°/27°). It hydrolyzes in water or in moist air to form hydrogen chloride and an insoluble "vinyl silicone" gel.

References

1. HURD: *J. Am. Chem. Soc.*, **67**, 1813 (1945).
2. USHAKOV and ITENBERG: *J. Gen. Chem. (U.S.S.R.)*, **7**, 2495 (1937); *cf.* *Chem. Abstracts*, **32**, 2083 (1938).
3. ROCHOW: *J. Am. Chem. Soc.*, **67**, 963 (1945).
4. KIPPING: *Proc. Chem. Soc.*, **20**, 15 (1904).

* The residue left in the distilling flask following the dehydrochlorination reaction has a bad odor and, upon cooling, sets to a hard resin that is almost impossible to remove. Disposal of the flask is recommended.

† Various other compounds may be present in this mixture. In one case, distillation from a modified Claisen flask resulted in a continuously rising temperature of distillation, beginning at about 58°. The portion from 90 to 95° amounted to the specified yield, leaving a higher-boiling residue in the flask. Clean separation evidently requires a more efficient column. On standing, a small amount of crystalline precipitate may appear in the redistilled vinyltrichlorosilane. (W.S.T.)

16. DIPHENYLSILANEDIOL

$$(C_6H_5)_2SiCl_2 + 2H_2O \rightarrow (C_6H_5)_2Si(OH)_2 + 2HCl$$

SUBMITTED BY CHARLES A. BURKHARD[*]
CHECKED BY E. G. ROCHOW[†] AND W. S. TATLOCK[†]

Diphenylsilanediol is an easily synthesized compound that finds use in the preparation of the cyclic diphenylsiloxane polymers ("phenyl silicone"). It may be prepared by hydrolyzing diphenyldichlorosilane, using a two-phase hydrolysis mixture consisting of toluene, tert-amyl alcohol, and water. The resulting diol is stable at room temperature. The diphenyldichlorosilane can be prepared by the reaction of chlorobenzene and silver-silicon alloy,[6] or by the Grignard reaction, involving interaction of a phenylmagnesium halide with silicon tetrachloride.[7]

Procedure

To a heterogeneous mixture of 77 ml. of toluene, 161 ml. of tert-amyl alcohol, and 666 ml. of water is added dropwise with stirring 200 g. of diphenyldichlorosilane mixed with 77 ml. of toluene. The temperature of the solution is maintained at 25°, preferably by using an internal cooling coil. About $\frac{1}{2}$ hour is required for addition of the chloride, after which the solution is stirred for another 10 minutes. The solution is then filtered by suction; the crystals are washed with water, until free from acid, and air-dried. These crystals are essentially free from polymeric materials. Further purification may be effected by dissolving the product in warm methylethyl ketone, adding chloroform until crystals form, warming gently to bring these back in solution, and setting aside the clear solution until crystallization has taken place. The yield is 156 g., or 93 per cent.

Properties

Diphenylsilanediol is a white, crystalline solid that melts at 148° with decomposition and readily dehydrates

* Research Laboratory, General Electric Company, Schenectady, N.Y.
† Harvard University, Cambridge, Mass.

thermally, or in the presence of catalysts, to form the cyclic condensation products hexaphenylcyclotrisiloxane and octaphenylcyclotetrasiloxane.

References

1. BURKHARD: *J. Am. Chem. Soc.*, **67**, 2173 (1945).
2. KIPPING: *Proc. Chem. Soc.*, **28**, 243 (1912).
3. KIPPING: *J. Chem. Soc.*, **101**, 2108 (1912).
4. KIPPING and ROBISON: *ibid.*, **105**, 484 (1914).
5. HYDE and DELONG: *J. Am. Chem. Soc.*, **63**, 1194 (1941).
6. ROCHOW and GILLIAM: *ibid.*, **67**, 1772 (1945).
7. KIPPING: *Proc. Chem. Soc.*, **20**, 15 (1904).

17. GERMANIUM(II) IODIDE

(Germanium diiodide)

$$GeI_4 + H_2O + H_3PO_2 \rightarrow GeI_2 + H_3PO_3 + 2HI$$

SUBMITTED BY LAURENCE S. FOSTER[*]
CHECKED BY THERALD MOELLER[†] AND LEO F. HENEGHAN[†]

Although germanium(II) iodide may be prepared by the reaction of germanium(II) sulfide with concentrated hydriodic acid,[1] the procedure is complicated by the rather involved preliminary preparation of the sulfide.[2] A somewhat simpler procedure, which also gives a higher yield, involves the direct reduction of germanium(IV) iodide with hypophosphorous acid in hydriodic acid solution. Germanium(IV) iodide is readily obtainable from the oxide.[3]

Procedure

Twenty grams of germanium(IV) iodide is placed in a 250-ml. three-necked flask provided with ground-glass joints. One opening is fitted with a reflux condenser, another with a mechanical stirrer, and the third with a glass stopper. Ten milliliters of colorless, 57 per cent hydriodic acid and 20 ml. of water are introduced, whereupon operation of the stirrer is begun. After the addition of 7.6 ml. of 50 per cent hypophosphorous acid (2 ml. in

---

[*] Brown University, Providence, R.I.
[†] University of Illinois, Urbana, Ill.

excess of the theoretical), the flask is closed with the glass stopper. The mixture is then heated to boiling under reflux. In a short time, the red crystals of germanium(IV) iodide will have been converted into the yellow plates of germanium(II) iodide.

The mixture is then cooled to 10° and the crystals are removed by filtration on a sintered-glass crucible. The crystals are washed on the filter with dilute hydriodic acid (1 part concentrated acid to 2 parts water) and dried *in vacuo* over phosphorus(V) oxide in an Abderhalden drier, using boiling toluene to keep the temperature at 110°. Any unreduced germanium(IV) iodide is removed by sublimation in this process. The yield is about 9 g. (75 per cent based upon germanium(IV) iodide).* Properties of germanium(II) have been described previously.[1]

References

1. FLOOD, FOSTER, and PIETRUSZA: INORGANIC SYNTHESES, **2**, 106 (1946).
2. FOSTER: *ibid.*, **2**, 102 (1946).
3. FOSTER and WILLISTON: *ibid.*, **2**, 112 (1946).

18. METHYLGERMANIUM TRIIODIDE

(Methyltriiodogermane)

$$GeI_2 + CH_3I \rightarrow CH_3GeI_3$$

SUBMITTED BY E. A. FLOOD,[†] K. L GODFREY,[†] AND L. S. FOSTER[†]
CHECKED BY A. W. LAUBENGAYER[‡] AND B. ALLEN[‡]

Methylgermanium triiodide is readily prepared by direct interaction of germanium(II) iodide with methyl iodide,

---

* Since germanium(II) iodide is appreciably soluble in water and in dilute acids, it may be desirable to recover the germanium remaining in solution. The filtrate, obtained after removal of germanium(II) iodide, is transferred to a 500-ml. pyrex, glass-stoppered retort and oxidized with 2 ml. of concentrated nitric acid. The liberated iodine is volatilized from the gently boiling mixture and may be collected. The residual solution is made 6 N in H^+ by addition of 18 N sulfuric acid, and saturated with hydrogen sulfide. Pure white germanium(IV) sulfide is precipitated.

† Brown University, Providence, R.I.
‡ Cornell University, Ithaca, N.Y.

using a procedure similar to that employed for the synthesis of ethylgermanium triiodide.[1] The starting material, germanium(II) iodide, may be produced conveniently from germanium(IV) oxide[3] or from germanium(IV) iodide by reduction with hypophosphorous acid (synthesis 17).

Procedure

Ten grams of germanium(II) iodide is introduced into a heavy-wall pyrex ampoule and attached by means of a

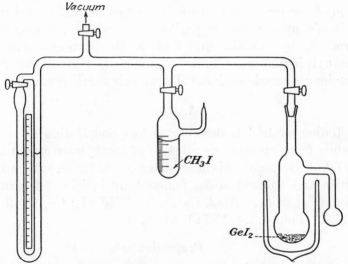

Fig. 13.   Apparatus for the preparation of methylgermanium triiodide.

ground joint to a glass vacuum system carrying a graduated reservoir of methyl iodide, as shown in Fig. 13. The ampoule is provided with a side tube into which excess methyl iodide may be distilled and recovered when the reaction is complete. After the air has been exhausted, the ampoule is immersed in a cooling mixture (Dry Ice and isopropyl alcohol), and 2.1 ml. of methyl iodide (4.8 g., representing a 10 per cent excess) is distilled in under its vapor pressure at room temperature (b.p. 42.5°). The neck of the ampoule is sealed and the tube is heated in an oven at 110° for at least 24 hours. Caution. *The initial pressure is high and the ampoule may explode if its walls are thin.* As reaction takes place, the yellow crystals of germanium(II) iodide disappear gradually, and a clear yellow liquid remains. If the iodide contains oxide, this will remain undissolved. When cooled the entire product becomes solid, unless too great an excess of methyl iodide has been used. After cooling, the excess methyl iodide is removed by immersing the side arm of the ampoule in a cooling mixture, and then sealing it off. The bottom portion of the reaction ampoule is cracked off and placed in a suitable apparatus for purification and recovery of the product by distillation. During this process residual methyl iodide may first be removed; nonvolatile contaminants remain behind. The yield is nearly quantitative.

Analysis

Iodine content is determined by precipitation as silver iodide from an aqueous solution of methylgermanium triiodide. Germanium is determined by oxidation with mixed nitric and sulfuric acids, followed by ignition to germanium(IV) oxide. *Anal.* Calcd. for CH_3GeI_3: Ge, 15.49; I, 81.29. Found: Ge, 15.7; I, 81.38.

Properties

Methylgermanium triiodide is a lemon-yellow solid (m.p. 48.5°). Its crystals are anisotropic, biaxial negative, and probably rhombohedral.[2] It is thermally stable, and may be distilled with no evidence of decomposition (b.p. 237° at 752 mm). The color deepens to red as the temperature rises, but returns to yellow as the sample cools. It is soluble in water with extensive hydrolysis, and is ammonolyzed in liquid ammonia. It is soluble in organic solvents and may be recrystallized from petroleum ether by cooling a solution, saturated at 50°, to −33° by means of a bath of liquid ammonia. It may be sublimed at 45° in a vacuum to give beautiful, large, clear yellow crystals.

Vacuum distillation is faster, however, and is preferred as a method of purification.

Methylgermanium triiodide hydrolyzes in a limited amount of water to a mass of white needles that apparently constitute a crystalline form of methylgermanium oxide. Refluxing methylgermanium triiodide with 30 per cent hydrogen peroxide, followed by sublimation of the liberated iodine, leaves an aqueous solution of the oxide from which a glassy solid may be obtained by evaporation. The glassy or amorphous material is a mixture of polymers of the empirical composition $CH_3GeO_{1.5}$; in dilute aqueous solution its molecular weight corresponds to the monomeric CH_3GeOOH but in concentrated solutions the condensed forms prevail. Hydrogen sulfide precipitates white methylgermanium sulfide from an acidified solution of the oxide, and hydrogen peroxide reconverts the sulfide to the oxide. Both compounds are difficult to oxidize completely, even at high temperatures.

References

1. FLOOD: *J. Am. Chem. Soc.*, **55**, 4935 (1933).
2. QUINN, ALONZO: Department of Geology, Brown University, Providence, R.I., private communication.
3. FLOOD, FOSTER, and PIETRUSZA: INORGANIC SYNTHESES, **2**, 106 (1946).

19. THE EXTRACTION OF HAFNIUM AND ZIRCONIUM FROM CYRTOLITE

SUBMITTED BY EDWIN M. LARSEN,* W. CONARD FERNELIUS,† AND LAURENCE L. QUILL‡
CHECKED BY WILLIAM CASTER, JR.,§ AND FRED BASOLO§

The lack of a convenient method for the separation of hafnium from zirconium has undoubtedly been the principal deterring factor in the development of the chemistry of hafnium. Methods that can be used for the separation

* University of Wisconsin, Madison, Wis.
† Pennsylvania State College, State College, Pa.
‡ Michigan State College, East Lansing, Mich.
§ Northwestern University, Evanston, Ill.

involve (1) the fractional crystallization of the hexa-fluorides,[1] or oxychlorides;[2] (2) the fractional precipitation of the phosphates,[3] or ethyl phosphates;[4] and (3) the fractional decomposition of complex ions of zirconium and hafnium formed with sulfuric acid, phosphoric acid, hydro-fluoric acid, dicarboxylic acids, α-hydroxy carboxylic acids, and polyhydroxy alcohols,[5] to yield the oxides or phosphates as precipitates.[6]

The following procedure involves the fractional precipitation of the phosphates in dilute acid solution. This direct precipitation procedure has not been used heretofore because of the gelatinous character of the usual phosphate precipitate, and the lack of a convenient method for converting the insoluble phosphates to soluble compounds for reprecipitation. These difficulties are overcome in the following process.

Raw Material

An altered zircon, cyrtolite, which is a hydrated zirconium silicate in which part of the zirconium is replaced by hafnium, and divalent and trivalent metals, is used as the raw material. This ore, although not very abundant, is used as the source material rather than the zircon or baddeleyite (1) because of its higher hafnium content (5 to 9 per cent compared to 2 per cent or less for the normal ores), and (2) because it is easily susceptible to acid attack. Ordinarily silicates are not easily attacked by acid treatment and must be handled by some fusion method. However, Urbain[7] reported successful extraction by sulfuric acid at 65° of malacon, an altered zircon, and other investigators have noted that cyrtolite[6,8] also yields to sulfuric acid treatment.

Procedure

A. EXTRACTION

The massive cyrtolite is crushed in a jaw crusher and pulverized in a ball mill. Material that passes through a 200-mesh screen is retained, while the coarser particles are returned to the ball mill for further treatment. Two hundred grams of 200-mesh ore and 400 g. of concentrated sulfuric acid are mixed in an 8-in. evaporating dish which is placed on a sand bath heated by Méker burners. After heating for about 20 minutes the temperature should have reached a maximum of 210 to 220°, and the mixture should begin to thicken. The heating process is continued for 10 minutes or until a stiff mud results. At this point heating is discontinued and the cracked ore is cooled before it is added to 1 l. of water in a 1.5-l. beaker. Twenty milliliters of a 10 per cent glue solution is added to aid in the coagulation and filtration of the insoluble residue. The solution is filtered on a Büchner funnel and the residue washed with 100 ml. of water. The filtrates are combined. Treatment of the residue with sulfuric acid under the same conditions should not result in any further loss in weight. If larger equipment is available the extraction may be run with multiples of the indicated quantities. The extraction of 1 kg. of ore should yield 5.5 l. of solution containing the equivalent of 600 g. of RO_2, 8 to 9 per cent of which is HfO_2. The solutions from combined extractions are analyzed for total acid, total RO_2 and HfO_2.

B. ANALYTICAL METHODS

Hafnium Content. The hafnium concentration is best determined by the method of Claasen[9] as modified by Schumb and Pittman,[6] Willard and Freund,[4] and the checkers of this synthesis. An aliquot of the zirconium hafnium solution that will provide about 1 g. of the oxide is diluted with water in a 250-ml. beaker. An excess of ammonium hydroxide is added to precipitate the hydroxide. The precipitate is filtered, washed free of sulfate, and then dissolved in 10 ml. of hot concentrated hydrochloric acid. The solution is placed in a 50-ml. beaker and is evaporated almost to dryness to dehydrate the silicic acid. The residue is treated with 15 ml. of hot 8 N hydrochloric acid and the insoluble material removed by filtration on a coarse paper.

The oxychloride[10] is recovered from this solution by warming to 70°, after which the solution is allowed to cool slowly. The oxychloride is removed by filtration on a porous-bottomed Selas* crucible, washed with ether until the yellow color has been removed completely, and then air-dried.

Approximately 1.5 g. of the oxychloride is placed in a 400-ml. beaker and is dissolved in 6 ml. of concentrated hydrochloric acid. The solution is treated with 7.5 ml. of 30 per cent hydrogen peroxide and heated to boiling. After decomposition of the peroxide, the solution is diluted to 200 ml. with water. Seventy-five milliliters of 20 per cent selenious acid is added to precipitate the basic selenites, which are digested on a steam bath for 12 hours or until the flocculent precipitate is completely converted to the dense granular mixture of the normal selenites. The precipitate is filtered on a Selas crucible, washed free of excess selenious acid with 2 l. of hot water, and then dried at 120 to 140° for 12 hours. Weighed portions (0.5 g.) of the dried, mixed selenites are then carefully ignited to the mixed oxides. The per cent of hafnia is determined from the formula:

$$\text{Per cent } HfO_2 = \frac{374.86[\text{wt. oxides} - 0.35702(\text{wt. selenites})]}{\text{wt. oxides}}$$

The percentage of hafnium may also be determined by measuring the density of the ignited mixed oxides. Since this method has been found to be unreliable[3] for mixtures containing more than 85 per cent hafnia, it is not recommended as a method of analysis.

Total Oxide, RO_2. An aliquot of the zirconium hafnium solution that will provide approximately 0.5 g. of the ignited oxide is diluted with water to 100 ml. and treated with ammonium hydroxide to precipitate the mixed hydroxides. The precipitate is filtered on quantitative paper, washed free of sulfate, placed in a weighed crucible, and ignited (900°) to constant weight in a muffle furnace or over a Fisher burner.

* No. 3001 microporous filter crucible. Selas, Philadelphia, Pa.

Total Acidity. A 1- to 2-ml. aliquot of the zirconium hafnium solution is diluted with 50 ml. of water in a 250-ml. beaker and titrated with 0.1 N sodium hydroxide to a phenolphthalein end point. From the titration data the total number of equivalents is calculated, and from the RO_2 and HfO_2 data, the number of equivalents due to RO_2. The difference in these values yields the excess acid concentration.

C. Precipitation of Zirconium Hafnium Phosphates

A sandy, easily filtered and washed phosphate precipitate is obtained by dispersing dilute solutions of the reactants into a large volume of hot (70 to 90°) dilute sulfuric acid.* Three solutions are required: (1) a 2 N sulfuric acid solution, which serves as the reaction medium; (2) a zirconium hafnium oxysulfate solution containing 2 to 5 per cent RO_2 in 2 N sulfuric acid, and (3) a 2 to 5 per cent phosphoric acid solution in 2 N sulfuric acid.

For large precipitations an earthenware crock is suitable (Fig. 14). In such cases, the acid liquor is heated to 75° by a Vitreosil immersion heater, B. The solution is kept in agitation by a motor-driven stirrer, shaft, and paddles, C, which are constructed of an acid-resistant material such as Hastelloy.

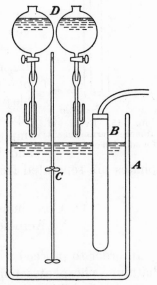

Fig. 14. Apparatus for precipitation of zirconium hafnium phosphates.

* The filterability of the phosphate precipitate has been found to depend to some extent upon the concentration of the final suspension. Experiments have shown that the best results are obtained when the final suspension contains not less than 0.015 or not more than 0.10 mols of phosphate per liter of solution.

The reagents (2) and (3) are added simultaneously by means of an atomizer arrangement (Fig. 15) into the hot 2 N sulfuric acid reaction medium. To obtain a satisfactory precipitate the reagents must be added at a rate not to exceed about 1 l. per hour. Care must be taken to add both reagents at an equivalent rate. The rate of flow is checked by means of a drop counter inserted below the stopcock of the separatory funnel, D. Since the rate of evaporation of the solution at 75° almost equals the rate of addition of the reagents, a constant volume of solution is maintained with some increase in the acid concentration. Inasmuch as zirconium and hafnium phosphates are among the most insoluble phosphates known, one complete precipitation serves to remove most of the impurities associated with the zirconium and hafnium. The precipitated phosphates are separated from the mother liquor by filtration.

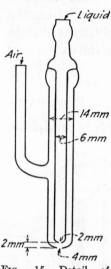

FIG. 15. Detail of atomizer arrangement for addition of reagents.

D. CONVERSION OF THE PHOSPHATES
TO ACID-SOLUBLE COMPOUNDS

In order to proceed with the fractionation, the zirconium hafnium phosphates must be converted into acid-soluble compounds. Digestion[3] of the moist phosphates with a mixture of sodium hydroxide and sodium peroxide yields a dense white peroxy compound, which can be washed free from the soluble phosphates, and which is soluble in acid with the evolution of oxygen. This reaction is utilized in the following procedure, except that 30 per cent hydrogen peroxide has been substituted for the sodium peroxide.

The precipitated phosphate mixture is transferred to a 4-l. beaker and mixed thoroughly with water to give a homogeneous paste containing about 1.2 mols of the phosphate (dry basis) per liter of slurry. Adsorbed acid is neutralized (litmus) with sodium hydroxide solution. The slurry is then cooled externally with ice to 10° and the calculated amount of 30 per cent hydrogen peroxide (1 l., 30 per cent H_2O_2 per mol of RO_2) is added. To this mixture is added, with stirring, a cold concentrated (40 g. per 100 g.) solution of sodium hydroxide (300 g. NaOH per mol of RO_2). After the mixture has been well stirred, the beaker is transferred to a hot plate, and the temperature of the mixture maintained at 50 to 70° for 3 hours. At the end of this time the intermediate soluble peroxyzirconate hafnate should be completely decomposed to the insoluble peroxy compounds.* The precipitate is allowed to settle, the supernatant liquor decanted, and replaced with an equal volume of phosphate-free 1 M ammonium sulfate solution.† The supernatant liquors and subsequent washes are filtered on a Büchner funnel using a filter paper suitable for fine precipitates. Washing by decantation is continued until the supernatant liquors no longer give a test for phosphate.‡ The entire precipitate is then transferred to the filter to remove the remainder of the wash liquor.

The precipitate is subsequently transferred to a beaker and dissolved in sufficient 1:1 sulfuric acid to give a 2 N sulfuric acid solution containing 2 to 5 per cent RO_2 when finally diluted with water. The solution is then boiled to decompose the peroxide. A clear solution results if the precipitate has been washed free of phosphate; if a precipitate appears, it is best separated from the mother liquor by centrifugation and re-treated in the prescribed manner. The final solution is analyzed for total oxide and HfO_2.

* To test for the completeness of the digestion, an aliquot of the supernatant liquor is transferred to a test tube, and heated to boiling; if no additional precipitate forms the reaction is complete.

† This may be prepared in large quantities from c.p. sulfuric acid and ammonium hydroxide.

‡ The ammonium molybdate test is used. Care must be taken that all the reagents are phosphate-free.

E. FRACTIONATION OF ZIRCONIUM AND HAFNIUM

The mechanics of fractionation are the same as for complete precipitation except that an insufficient amount of precipitant is used. To determine what the optimum cut-off value for a given hafnia concentration should be, and to determine also what enrichment may be expected in each

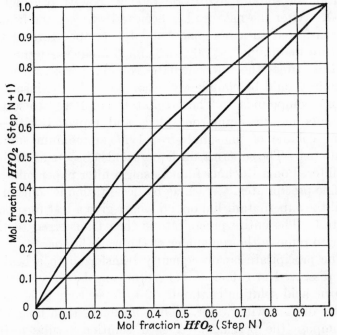

FIG. 16. Comparison of composition at step N + 1 and step N.

step, the experimental data for this procedure have been treated by the method of Willard.[4] The results are expressed in Figs. 16 and 17. Thus, knowing the hafnium content, the mol per cent of RO_2 to be precipitated is obtained from Fig. 17. The number of grams of phosphoric acid necessary to precipitate this mol per cent of RO_2 as the phosphate is diluted with 2 N sulfuric acid to give the same volume as that of the 2 to 5 per cent zirconium hafnium oxysulfate which is also in 2 N acid. The two solutions are then added to the hot sulfuric acid solution at the same rate. At times it is more convenient to dilute the phosphoric acid to only a fraction of the volume of the zirconium oxysulfate solution to prevent excessive dilution of the phosphoric acid; the rate of addition of the phosphoric acid must then be correspondingly reduced. Care must be taken that the rate of addition of the reagents is such that a constant fraction of the total RO_2 is removed throughout the precipitation. Since the hafnium concen-

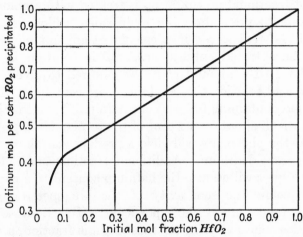

Fig. 17. Comparison of optimum mol fraction of combined oxides precipitated and composition of starting material.

trates in the insoluble fraction, the precipitate is filtered, converted to the acid-soluble peroxy compounds, and then dissolved to yield a solution suitable for further fractionation.

By using the prediction curve (Fig. 16) it should be possible, theoretically, to proceed through the fractionation with no analyses other than the initial analysis. However, since actual operating conditions are not as reproducible as would be desired, deviations from the predicted enrichment are observed. Since small changes are additive an appreciable error may result within a few steps. It is therefore necessary to determine the hafnium content at frequent intervals.

Starting with a raw material containing 0.1 mol fraction

HfO_2, it is possible to obtain, in a series of seven fractionations, about a 10 per cent yield of a product with 0.9 mol fraction HfO_2. Mother liquors of approximately equivalent concentration from the various steps are combined for re-treatment.

F. THE PREPARATION OF LOW-HAFNIUM ZIRCONIA

To prepare low-hafnium zirconia, the mother liquor from the first fractional precipitation is treated with ammonium hydroxide to precipitate the hydroxides, which are then filtered and redissolved in a calculated amount of moderately concentrated sulfuric acid. This solution is then diluted with the amount of water required to give a 2 N sulfuric acid solution that contains 5 per cent RO_2. From a fraction containing 0.7 per cent hafnium,* one fractionation in which about 60 per cent of the total oxide is precipitated as the phosphate will yield a product containing only 0.2 per cent hafnium. Additional fractionations of the mother liquor will reduce the hafnium content to a concentration below the sensitivity of the arc spectrographic method used (about 0.05 per cent Hf). Because the impurities concentrate in the most soluble fraction, a complete phosphate precipitation is made on the final solution, the precipitate is washed with 2 N sulfuric acid, and then converted to the peroxy compound. For final purification, the acid-soluble peroxy compound is dissolved in hydrochloric acid, and the oxychloride prepared according to the procedure of Young and Arch.[10] The oxychloride may then be used as a starting material for the preparation of any other zirconium compound.

References

1. DEBOER and VAN ARKEL: Z. anorg. allgem. Chem., 141, 2848 (1924).
2. COSTER and VON HEVESY: U.S. patent 1666440 (April 17, 1928); cf. Chem. Abstracts, 22, 2037 (1928).
3. LARSEN, FERNELIUS, and QUILL: Anal. Chem., 15, 512 (1943).

* Arc spectrographic analyses by Cyrus Feldman, Oak Ridge National Laboratories, Oak Ridge, Tenn.

4. WILLARD and FREUND: *Anal. Chem.*, **18**, 195 (1946).
5. DEBOER: *Z. anorg. allgem. Chem.*, **165**, 1 (1927).
6. SCHUMB and PITTMAN: *Anal. Chem.*, **14**, 312 (1942).
7. MARQUIS, URBAIN, and URBAIN: *Compt. rend.*, **180**, 1377 (1923).
8. VAN OSDALL: thesis, Ohio State University, 1939.
9. CLAASEN: *Z. anal. Chem.*, **117**, 252 (1939).
10. YOUNG and ARCH: INORGANIC SYNTHESES, **2**, 121 (1946).

CHAPTER V

20. NITROGEN(V) OXIDE

(Nitrogen Pentoxide, Dinitrogen Pentoxide, Nitric Anhydride)

$$2HONO_2 + P_2O_5 \rightarrow N_2O_5 + 2HPO_3$$

SUBMITTED BY N. S. GRUENHUT,* M. GOLDFRANK,* M. L. CUSHING,* AND G. V. CAESAR*
CHECKED BY P. D. CAESAR† AND C. SHOEMAKER†

Nitrogen(V) oxide appears to have been first prepared in 1840[1] by passing dry chlorine over dry silver nitrate heated on a water bath, the oxide being collected in solid form in a tube immersed in a freezing mixture. Subsequently, it was prepared by various investigators[2-6] through dehydration of concentrated nitric acid by phosphorus(V) oxide. A third method involves oxidation of the equilibrium mixture NO_2-N_2O_4 with ozone.[7,8] Nitrogen(V) oxide is also reported to form when a mixture of oxygen and nitrogen is passed through an electric arc at high voltages.[9]

The method described below represents a modification

* Stein Hall Research Laboratory, New York, N.Y.
† University of Illinois, Urbana, Ill.

78

of the procedure developed by Russ and Pokorny.[4] It was designed primarily to obtain increased yields of crude nitrogen(V) oxide for nitration experiments.[10] The distinguishing feature of the method is an initial freezing of the nitric acid and a slow settling of a thick cover of phosphorus(V) oxide into the melting acid. In earlier methods, phosphorus(V) oxide was added to the liquid acid.

Procedure

The apparatus for the preparation of nitrogen(V) oxide is shown in Fig. 18. Oxygen is bubbled into bottle *A* con-

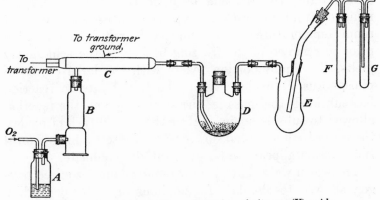

FIG. 18. Apparatus for the preparation of nitrogen(V) oxide.

taining sulfuric acid, through a trap *B* containing glass wool, into an ozonizer *C*, thence to a three-necked reaction flask *D*, receiver *E*, trap *F*, and bubble counter *G*. The apparatus is set up in a large hood. Ground-glass connections are advisable throughout, but if these are not available, cork stoppers coated with paraffin may be used.*

If "white nitric acid" is not available, it is advisable to bubble dry oxygen through nitric acid (sp. gr. about 1.50) for several hours. The acid is then thoroughly chilled in a deep-freeze unit.

* Rubber stoppers and rubber tubing must be eliminated because of attack by ozone. Saran tubing has been found to be fairly satisfactory, especially in that portion of the apparatus where tubing comes in contact with ozone.

About 100 g. of the chilled acid is placed in reaction flask
D, receiver E is disconnected, and oxygen is bubbled
through the acid again for 10 minutes. The acid in D is
then frozen solid (*important*) by immersion of the flask in
Dry Ice and alcohol. The passage of oxygen is continued
during this operation. Receiver E is also immersed in an
alcohol and Dry Ice cooling bath and is connected to the
system; oxygen is allowed to pass through for several
minutes to remove moist air.

About 125 g. of phosphorus(V) oxide is quickly spread
over the surface of the frozen acid in D, the flask stopper
sealed tight, the freezing bath of Dry Ice and alcohol
removed from under D and replaced with a water bath at
room temperature. The ozonizer is put into operation
prior to removal of the freezing bath. As the acid slowly
melts, the liquid portion reacts with the large excess of
phosphorus(V) oxide. When the initial intense reaction
has subsided, the mass is stirred quickly and the reaction
allowed to subside again. After the second rush of oxides,
the water bath is heated slowly to 40° for several hours until
the reaction appears to be substantially complete.

The warm water bath is now removed and ozonized oxygen allowed to circulate for an hour or more, depending
upon the required degree of purity of nitrogen(V) oxide.
The N_2O_4 content* will also be reduced (1) if ample time
is allowed between each of the first two periods of maximum
reaction, and (2) by slower and intermittent warming.

A yield of 42 g. is obtained, corresponding to approximately 50 per cent of theory based upon a nitric acid varying between 96 and 100 per cent in concentration. Higher
yields may be obtained at the expense of purity.

* An efficient source of ozone is necessary to reduce to a minimum the
N_2O_4 content of the product. The checkers employed a "Siemens' Form
Ozone Generator" purchased from the Central Scientific Company, Chicago,
Ill. With slow and careful distillation, it is possible to dispense with the
ozonizer C, provided that an N_2O_4 content of 10 to 20 per cent in the sublimed crystals is not objectionable.[10]

Properties

Nitrogen(V) oxide is a white, crystalline, unstable solid that sublimes readily just above room temperature.[8] It undergoes a first-order decomposition reaction into oxygen and the equilibrium mixture NO_2-N_2O_4. It is readily soluble in cold chloroform (a convenient method of using it) without appreciable reaction and, to a lesser extent, in carbon tetrachloride. Crude nitrogen(V) oxide in chloroform can be stored for as long as one week at $-20°$ without excessive decomposition. It is an extremely rapid, efficient, and safe nitrating agent in chloroform solution, when used in the presence of sodium fluoride as an adsorbent for the nitric acid by-product,[10] and offers interesting possibilities for continuous processes of nitration.

References

1. DEVILLE: *Compt. rend.*, **28**, 257, 1449 (1840).
2. WEBER: *Pogg. Ann.*, **147**, 113 (1872).
3. BERTHELOT: *Bull. soc. chim.*, **21**, 53 (1874).
4. RUSS and POKORNY: *Monatsh.*, **34**, 1051 (1913).
5. DANIELS and BRIGHT: *J. Am. Chem. Soc.*, **42**, 1131 (1920).
6. BERL and SAENGER: *Monatsh.*, **53–54**, 1036 (1929).
7. HELBIG: *Atti accad. Lincei*, [11] II, 311 (1902).
8. YOST and RUSSELL: "Systematic Inorganic Chemistry," Prentice-Hall, Inc., New York, 1944.
9. EHRLICH and RUSS: *Monatsh.*, **32**, 917 (1911).
10. CAESAR and GOLDFRANK: *J. Am. Chem. Soc.*, **68**, 372 (1946).

21. HYDROXYLAMMONIUM SALTS

SUBMITTED BY PHILIP F. TRYON*
CHECKED BY W. V. FACKLER, JR.,† AND L. F. AUDRIETH†

Hydroxylammonium salts are reagents usually employed as sources of hydroxylamine for various inorganic and organic reactions. The chloride and sulfate are the better known commercially available salts obtained by the hydrolysis of the nitroparaffins. The phosphate,[1-3] arsenate,[4]

* Commercial Solvents Corporation, Terre Haute, Ind.
† University of Illinois, Urbana, Ill.

and oxalate[1,5] represent three sparingly soluble salts that can be obtained from the chloride or the sulfate by metathesis with the corresponding sodium salts.

Procedure

A. HYDROXYLAMMONIUM PHOSPHATE

$$3(NH_3OH)Cl + H_3PO_4 + 3NaOH$$
$$\rightarrow (NH_3OH)_3PO_4 + 3NaCl + 3H_2O$$

A mixture of 210 g. (3 mols) of hydroxylammonium chloride and 200 ml. of water is warmed to about 40° to dissolve the salt. The solution is filtered to remove any sediment, if necessary, and transferred to a 1500-ml. beaker. A mechanical stirrer and a thermometer are introduced into the solution. An empty cooling bath is placed around the beaker. The stirrer is placed in operation and stirring is continued throughout the synthesis of the compound. One hundred fifteen grams of 85 per cent phosphoric acid (1 mol) is next added rapidly.* A cooled solution of 120 g. of sodium hydroxide (3 mols) in 400 ml. of water is then added from a dropping funnel at a rapid dropwise rate.† The hydroxylammonium phosphate usually starts to crystallize toward the end of the addition. When all of the sodium hydroxide solution has been added, the crystal slurry is cooled to 15° by use of the cooling bath. The crystals are separated from the mother liquor by filtration through a 350-ml. sintered-glass funnel, and washed with three 100-ml. portions of water. Purification by washing is best accomplished by breaking the vacuum, and stirring the crystals in the funnel with each separate portion of wash water. If high purity is not necessary, the wet crystals are dried in air overnight, and then *in vacuo* over phos-

---

* Occasionally, some of the hydroxylammonium chloride will crystallize at this point, but it all redissolves during the next step.

† The temperature of the solution will generally rise no higher than 70° toward the end of this addition. If it should go above 75°, ice and water are placed in the cooling bath in order to prevent the possible gaseous decomposition of the hydroxylamine salt.

phorus(V) oxide. Approximately 175 to 180 g. of a crude product with a purity of about 95 per cent is readily obtainable.

Purification can be effected by dissolving the wet crystals (total yield of crude product) in 1750 ml. of water at 80 to 85°, cooling to about 15° to effect crystallization, followed by filtration and washing. The recrystallized compound is dried as recommended above. About 140 to 145 g. (72 per cent) of a product with a purity of 98 per cent is obtainable in this manner.

B. HYDROXYLAMMONIUM ARSENATE

$$3(NH_3OH)Cl + Na_2HAsO_4 \cdot 7H_2O + NaOH$$
$$\rightarrow (NH_3OH)_3AsO_4 + 3NaCl + 8H_2O$$

The conditions for preparation of the arsenate are similar to those specified for the phosphate, except that a solution of 312 g. (1 mol) of disodium hydrogen arsenate 7-hydrate in 300 ml. of water (heated to 50° to effect solution) is substituted for the phosphoric acid. Hydroxylammonium arsenate may begin to crystallize before all of the arsenate has been added. An uncooled solution of 40 g. of sodium hydroxide (1 mol) in 100 ml. of water is added to effect neutralization. Three 150-ml. portions of water are used to wash the crude product. The yield is 200 to 210 g. of a product whose purity is approximately 95 per cent based on the hydroxylamine content. Purification can be effected by recrystallization of the arsenate from eight times its weight of water. Recovery amounts to about 145 g. (approximately 60 per cent) of a product with a purity of 98 per cent or better.

C. HYDROXYLAMMONIUM OXALATE

$$2(NH_3OH)Cl + H_2C_2O_4 \cdot 2H_2O + 2NaOH$$
$$\rightarrow (NH_3OH)_2C_2O_4 + 2NaCl + 4H_2O$$

The method for preparation of the oxalate is similar in principle to that used for the corresponding phosphate, the solution of hydroxylammonium chloride being somewhat more dilute [140 g. (2 mols) in 400 ml. of water]. While this solution is being stirred mechanically, 126 g. of crystalline oxalic acid 2-hydrate (1 mol) is added all at once. The crystals of acid do not all dissolve. After a few minutes, a solution of 80 g. of sodium hydroxide (2 mols) in 200 ml. of water is added at a rapid dropwise rate. A considerable amount of the hydroxylammonium oxalate will crystallize during this addition. The hot slurry is stirred for about 30 minutes, and is then cooled to about 15° and filtered. The crystals are washed with three 100-ml. portions of water. The crude product, weighing about 130 g., will generally contain about 10 per cent oxalic acid. It can be purified by recrystallization from about eight times its weight of water with an average yield of 95 g. (60 per cent) of a product whose purity by analysis will be better than 99 per cent.

Analysis

Analysis for the hydroxylamine content is effected by the Raschig method. The recommended procedure is a modification of the method given by Scott.[6] Approximately 0.1 g. of sample is dissolved in 75 ml. of water in an Erlenmeyer flask and 30 ml. of a saturated solution of iron(III) ammonium sulfate is added, followed by 10 ml. of 50 per cent sulfuric acid. The solution is boiled for 10 minutes, treated with approximately 5 to 10 ml. of phosphoric acid to reduce the color, then diluted with 200 ml. of water and titrated immediately with standard permanganate solution.

Properties

The normal hydroxylammonium salts of phosphoric, arsenic, and oxalic acids are colorless crystalline compounds. They are insoluble in organic solvents, and only sparingly soluble in water at room temperature. Some solubility values from the literature are given below. The solubility of the arsenate and the decomposition points of the three salts were determined on the recrystallized material prepared in accordance with directions given in this synthesis.

Property	Hydroxylammonium salt		
	Phosphate	Arsenate	Oxalate
Solubility, g. per 100 ml. of water:			
20°	1.9 (3)	2.4	1.4 (5)
40°	4.2		
60°	8.4		
80°	15.3		
Decomposition point, approx	165°	135°	180°

Hydroxylammonium phosphate serves as a convenient reagent for the preparation of oximes; the saturated aqueous solution has a pH of about 5, the pH of maximum rate of oxime formation.

References

1. LOSSEN: *Ann. Suppl.*, **6**, 230 (1868).
2. UHLENHUTH: *Ann.*, **311**, 117 (1900).
3. ADAMS: *Am. Chem. J.*, **28**, 198 (1902).
4. KOHLSCHÜTTER and HOFMANN: *Ann.*, **307**, 314 (1899).
5. SIMON: *Bull. soc. chim.* (3) **33**, 412 (1905).
6. SCOTT: "Standard Methods of Chemical Analysis," 5th ed., Vol. 1, p. 647, D. Van Nostrand Company, Inc., New York, 1939.

22. THE POLY- AND METAPHOSPHATES AND THE STRONG PHOSPHORIC ACIDS

By L. F. AUDRIETH* AND R. N. BELL†

The sodium phosphates, polyphosphates, and metaphosphates, the preparation of which is described in this volume (see syntheses 24 to 26), represent a diversified group of compounds; their relationships are most easily elucidated by a consideration of their structures.[1] The structural unit that characterizes all phosphates is the PO_4 tetrahedron, the phosphorus atom being surrounded tetra-

* University of Illinois, Urbana, Ill.
† Victor Chemical Works Research Laboratory, Chicago Heights, Ill.

TABLE I

Acid	Name	Structure of the ion
A. Linear Polyphosphates		
H_3PO_4	Orthophosphoric	$\left[\begin{array}{c} O \\ \mid \\ O-P-O \\ \mid \\ O \end{array} \right]^{3-}$
$H_4P_2O_7$	Pyrophosphoric (diphosphoric)	$\left[\begin{array}{c} O \quad\quad O \\ \mid \quad\quad \mid \\ O-P-O-P-O \\ \mid \quad\quad \mid \\ O \quad\quad O \end{array} \right]^{4-}$
$H_5P_3O_{10}$	Triphosphoric (tripolyphosphoric)	$\left[\begin{array}{c} O \quad\quad O \quad\quad O \\ \mid \quad\quad \mid \quad\quad \mid \\ O-P-O-P-O-P-O \\ \mid \quad\quad \mid \quad\quad \mid \\ O \quad\quad O \quad\quad O \end{array} \right]^{5-}$
B. Cyclic Metaphosphates		
$H_3P_3O_9$	Trimetaphosphoric (trimeric metaphosphoric)	
$H_4P_4O_{12}$	Tetrametaphosphoric (tetrameric metaphosphoric)	

hedrally by four oxygen atoms. The sharing of oxygen atoms between two or more phosphate tetrahedra gives rise to (1) two series of crystalline phosphates represented by the linear polyphosphates and the cyclic metaphosphates, and (2) a whole range of phosphate glasses. The known crystalline poly- and metaphosphates are listed in Table I, together with the structures of the respective ions or groups.

Preparation. Conversion of orthophosphates into poly- and metaphosphates (and into the phosphate glasses) is accomplished in all known cases by high-temperature reactions. Conversion reactions leading to these products may be regarded as examples of polyanionic aggregation (commonly called "molecular dehydration"). These reactions are not unlike similar ones in which increase in the hydrogen-ion concentration of solutions of chromates (also molybdates, tungstates, and vanadates) causes their conversion successively into di-, tri-, and tetrachromates.[2,3] There is one significant difference, however, in that the polyanionic aggregation of the phosphates does not take place in aqueous solution, but only at higher temperatures either in the solid state or upon fusion. Equations that are usually employed to represent these reactions are given in Table II. Since these do not reveal the true nature of the reactions as acid-base phenomena, they have been rewritten in parentheses as involving reactions between the hydrogen ion and the phosphate ion. It is evident that the extent of polymerization is definitely a function of acidity, that is, of the ratio of hydrogen ion to phosphate ion.

TABLE II. PREPARATION OF POLY- AND METAPHOSPHATES

	Ratio H^+/PO_4^{3-}
1. $2HPO_4^- \rightarrow P_2O_7^{4-} + H_2O$	1.00
$(2H^+ + 2PO_4^{3-} \rightarrow P_2O_7^{4-} + H_2O)$	
2. $H_2PO_4^- + 2HPO_4^- \rightarrow P_3O_{10}^{5-} + 2H_2O$	1.33
$(4H^+ + 3PO_4^{3-} \rightarrow P_3O_{10}^{5-} + 2H_2O)$	
3. $xH_2PO_4^- \rightarrow xH_2O + x(PO_3)^{-*}$	2.00
$(2H^+ + PO_4^{3-} \rightarrow PO_3^- + H_2O)$	

* Where $x(PO_3)^- = (P_3O_9)^{3-}$, $(P_4O_{12})^{4-}$, polymetaphosphate glass and other possible metaphosphates.

Thus, fusion or heating of a monohydrogen phosphate will cause aggregation to proceed only as far as the pyrophosphate stage (synthesis 24) while triphosphate (synthesis 25) is obtainable in a more acidic medium, such as is furnished by a 2:1 molar mixture of mono- and dihydrogen phosphate. In a still more acidic medium, as in the case of dihydrogen phosphate, heating leads to formation of various metaphosphates. The trimetaphosphate (synthesis 26A) is obtained at moderate temperatures (400 to 500°), whereas the polymetaphosphate glass (synthesis 26B) is produced by heating to fusion at still higher temperatures (above 620°).

Fusion of any sodium phosphate with a $Na_2O:P_2O_5$ ratio varying from 1:1 to 5:3, followed by rapid chilling, results in the formation of the so-called "phosphate glasses." Such products dissolve in water to give solutions of polyanionic aggregates with ionic weights ranging up to the equivalent of 500 PO_3 units, and possibly even higher. The best known example of this class of materials is Graham's salt. It has commonly been called "hexametaphosphate." Recent investigations have shown that there is absolutely no justification for this name. It is even doubtful that any discrete unit consisting of 6 PO_3 groups is present in such a product. Various physical methods have been used to show that solutions of phosphate glasses contain aggregates of high ionic weight. Fractionation may be accomplished by the portionwise addition of an organic solvent such as acetone to an aqueous solution.[4] The first few fractions, containing the least soluble components, are found to have extremely high ionic weights. As more and more of the organic solvent is added to the residual solution, fractions are precipitated with smaller and smaller ionic weights. Average ionic weights of polymetaphosphates in such solutions vary from 10,000 to 25,000.[5-7]

The greater the state of aggregation (condensation polymerization), the more acidic are the poly- and metaphosphates.[3] Reference should again be made in this particular instance to the analogous behavior of the polychromates. Addition of a base to solutions of the polychromates causes their degradation to simpler aggregates, eventually to the chromate ion itself. This analogy may be carried over to the phosphate system; the polymetaphosphate glasses may be looked upon as anionic acids. Anionic bases will effect depolymerization to ortho- and pyrophosphates. Fused Graham's salt has long been used in analytical chemistry in the well-known "phosphate bead test" for the qualitative detection of various metallic oxides. These dissolve in the metaphosphate glass to form varicolored metallic ortho- and pyrophosphates.[8,9] Fusion of sodium sulfide with sodium polymetaphosphate is claimed to afford a convenient method for the preparation of the monothioorthophosphate.[10] Fusion of equimolecular weights of sodium fluoride with sodium polymetaphosphate results in formation of sodium monofluophosphate (synthesis 27).

Hydrolysis. All of the polyphosphates and metaphosphates undergo reaction with water. Such reactions have commonly been termed "reversion" reactions, and, if carried out under appropriate conditions, will cause depolymerization of poly- and metaphosphates to simple orthophosphate ions. In these reactions, water appears to act as a base with respect to the higher poly- and metaphosphates. A summary of the principal hydrolytic or reversion reactions of the various poly- and metaphosphates is presented in Table III.[11]

The Phosphoric Acids. Only two of the simple phosphoric acids have been prepared in the crystalline state, namely, orthophosphoric acid[12] and pyrophosphoric acid (synthesis 23). Several of the others have been prepared in dilute aqueous solution by treatment of the sodium salts with exchange resins containing replaceable hydrogen, or by treatment of the appropriate metallic salt with hydrogen sulfide.

It is significant, however, that the so-called "strong" phosphoric acids, those having a phosphorus(V) oxide content higher than 72.4 per cent [which corresponds to the phosphorus(V) oxide content of orthophosphoric acid], are mixtures of poly- and metaphosphoric acids, the compositions being functions of the phosphorus(V) oxide content. These strong phosphoric acids may be obtained by (1) high-temperature dehydration of orthophosphoric acid, (2) careful hydration of phosphorus(V) oxide, and (3) treatment of 85 per cent orthophosphoric acid with phosphorus(V) oxide and subsequent heating.

TABLE III. HYDROLYSIS REACTIONS

In Water

"Hexametaphosphate"	$3(NaPO_3)_6 + 12H_2O \rightarrow 2(NaPO_3)_3 + 12NaH_2PO_4$
Trimetaphosphate	$(NaPO_3)_3 + H_2O \rightarrow Na_3H_2P_3O_{10}$ $Na_3H_2P_3O_{10} + 2H_2O \rightarrow 3NaH_2PO_4$
Triphosphate	$Na_5P_3O_{10} + H_2O \rightarrow Na_3HP_2O_7 + Na_2HPO_4$
Pyrophosphates	$Na_2H_2P_2O_7 + H_2O \rightarrow 2NaH_2PO_4$ $Na_3HP_2O_7 + H_2O \rightarrow Na_2HPO_4 + NaH_2PO_4$ $Na_4P_2O_7 + H_2O \rightarrow 2Na_2HPO_4$

In 1 per cent NaOH *Solution*

Trimetaphosphate	$(NaPO_3)_3 + 2NaOH \rightarrow Na_5P_3O_{10} + H_2O$

Figure 19 depicts the compositions of the strong phosphoric acids.[13] A strong phosphoric acid containing 82 per cent phosphorus(V) oxide is a mixture consisting of ortho-, pyro-, tri-, and "hexameta-" phosphoric acids, and in addition a not unappreciable percentage of some yet-to-be-identified constituent. The compositions of the various strong phosphoric acids were determined by neutralization of the products with cold aqueous solutions of sodium hydroxide followed by analyses using the methods that are outlined below.

It is quite apparent that the strong phosphoric acids are not to be regarded as mixtures of orthophosphoric acid containing excesses of phosphorus(V) oxide. In this respect, the strong phosphoric acids differ markedly from "oleum" or fuming sulfuric acid which can be represented as containing an excess of sulfur trioxide. This difference appears to have been overlooked by a great many investigators who have concerned themselves with the phosphorylation of organic compounds.

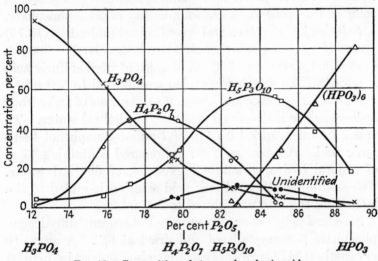

Fig. 19. Composition of strong phosphoric acids.

Method of Analysis for Mixtures of Soluble Phosphates.

Quantitative estimation of the compounds of simple mixtures of phosphates, polyphosphates, and polymetaphosphates can be effected without too much difficulty. Determinations of orthophosphate, pyrophosphate, triphosphate, and so-called "hexametaphosphate" are usually made on mixtures of soluble phosphates. Total phosphorus content is also determined by hydrolyzing all other phosphates to orthophosphoric acid. No distinctive analytical methods are, however, available for the direct quantitative determination of the cyclic metaphosphates.

1. Preparation of the Sample. A stock solution of the sample is made by dissolving 2.5 g. in distilled water at room temperature and diluting to a volume of 250 ml. Aliquots of suitable sizes are taken from this solution for the determination of the phosphates. When heterogeneous mixtures are to be analyzed, it may be necessary to weigh out a larger sample and to dilute proportionately.

2. Reagents. *a. Orthophosphate.*[24] Two reagent solutions must be prepared beforehand in addition to a standard solution that contains a known quantity of orthophosphate.

Solution 1. Eighteen and seventy-five hundredths (18.75) grams of c.p. ammonium molybdate is dissolved in 300 ml. of distilled water, and 150 ml. of concentrated sulfuric acid is added. The solution is cooled and diluted to 500 ml.

Solution 2. Three and one-half (3.5) grams of anhydrous sodium sulfite is dissolved in 50 ml. of distilled water. To this solution is added 0.75 g. of 1-amino-2-naphthol-4-sulfonic acid. Another solution is prepared containing 45 g. of sodium hydrogen sulfite in 400 ml. of distilled water. The sulfite-naphthol-sulfonic acid solution is added to the latter and the mixture diluted to 500 ml.

Standard Phosphate Solution. Potassium dihydrogen phosphate is recrystallized and dried at 85°. A quantity of exactly 0.3472 g. of this substance is dissolved in distilled water, and the solution is diluted to 250 ml. Twenty-five milliliters of this stock solution, when diluted to 250 ml., constitutes a standard solution, 1 ml. of which equals 0.1 mg. of H_3PO_4.

b. Pyro- and Triphosphates. The following solutions are required: (1) sodium hydroxide solution, 0.1 N; (2) hydrochloric acid solution, 0.2 N; (3) zinc sulfate solution, 12.5 per cent solution of $ZnSO_4 \cdot 7H_2O$ adjusted to pH 3.8.

c. Polymetaphosphate (Hexametaphosphate). Two solutions are required: (1) hydrochloric acid solution, 1.0 N; (2) barium chloride solution, 10 per cent solution.

3. Apparatus. In order to carry out the analyses outlined in detail below, it is necessary to have available a photoelectric colorimeter and a glass electrode pH meter and titration assembly.

Procedure

Orthophosphate.[14] An aliquot of the stock sample solution is taken that does not contain more than 0.4 mg. of phosphate. It will usually be necessary to withdraw a 10-ml. sample of the solution and dilute to 100 ml. One milliliter of the latter represents an aliquot that will contain in the neighborhood of 1.0 mg.* The aliquot is placed in a 25-ml. graduated cylinder and diluted to approximately 15 ml. Half-milliliter portions each of reagents (1) and (2) are next added. The sample is diluted to 25 ml. and mixed thoroughly. After it has stood for 10 minutes at room temperature (25 to 30°) the intensity of the blue color is measured on a photoelectric colorimeter. A blank should be run on the reagents and this figure should be used in adjusting the zero point on the colorimeter. The orthophosphate content is read from curves prepared from standard orthophosphate solutions. A red filter (Corning No. 244) increases the sensitivity of the determination.†

Pyro- and Triphosphates.[16] A 50-ml. aliquot (0.5 g.) of the sample is adjusted to pH 3.8 and diluted to 100 ml. (±2.0 ml.). The pH of this solution is readjusted after dilution if necessary. Seventy milliliters of the zinc sulfate reagent is added and the solution titrated back to pH 3.8 with 0.1 N sodium hydroxide.‡ Any pyrophosphate that may be present in the sample will have been precipitated as zinc pyrophosphate. After settling, the precipitate is filtered, washed lightly, and then purified in the following manner: The precipitate is dissolved in 15 to

---

* If the sample is too high in orthophosphate, a smaller aliquot must be taken.

† The color developed by this method is not sufficient for accurate visual comparison. If visual methods are used, the method of Bell and Doisy[15] should be followed.

‡ Addition to zinc sulfate results in the precipitation of zinc pyrophosphate and the formation of a complex sodium zinc triphosphate. Formation of both of these substances is accompanied by liberation of hydrogen ions. Titration with sodium hydroxide, therefore, effects neutralization of sulfuric acid liberated by both pyrophosphate and triphosphate.

20 ml. of 0.2 N hydrochloric acid and the solution diluted to 150 to 200 ml. volume; 25 ml. of zinc sulfate reagent is added and the pH is brought back to 3.8 with 0.1 N sodium hydroxide. The precipitate is allowed to settle and is filtered and washed with distilled water at room temperature. The precipitate is ignited, first at 400 to 500° and then at 700 to 800°, and weighed as $Zn_2P_2O_7$. The pyrophosphate content of the sample is calculated from the weight of zinc pyrophosphate; the triphosphate content is calculated from the titration after correction has been made for the titration equivalent of the pyrophosphate. The following factors are employed:

$$\text{g. } Zn_2P_2O_7 \times 0.572 = \text{g. } P_2O_7$$
$$\times 0.584 = \text{g. } H_4P_2O_7$$
$$\times 0.872 = \text{g. } Na_4P_2O_7$$
$$\times 65.5 = \text{ml. } 0.1 \text{ } N \text{ NaOH due to pyrophosphate}$$

Balance of titration:
$$\text{ml. of } 0.1 \text{ } N \text{ NaOH} \times 0.0177 = \text{g. } P_3O_{10}$$
$$\times 0.0181 = \text{g. } H_5P_3O_{10}$$
$$\times 0.0258 = \text{g. } Na_5P_3O_{10}$$

The factors shown above for triphosphate are empirical factors applicable only when the concentration of zinc sulfate in the titrated solution is as recommended.

Polymetaphosphate (Hexametaphosphate).[17] A 10-ml. aliquot (0.1 g.) of the sample solution diluted to 50 ml. is acidified to methyl orange with 1.0 N hydrochloric acid, and 0.5 ml. excess is added. Barium polymetaphosphate is precipitated by slowly adding 15 ml. of 10 per cent barium chloride reagent while stirring. When the precipitate has settled, it is filtered off and washed with 0.1 per cent barium chloride solution. The precipitate is dissolved in 20 to 30 ml. of 50 per cent nitric acid and hydrolyzed by boiling for 20 to 30 minutes. The resulting orthophosphate is precipitated as ammonium phosphomolybdate; the phosphorus content of the latter is determined as outlined in the following paragraph for total phosphorus, and calculated as polymetaphosphate.

Total phosphorus (as P_2O_5). A 10-ml. aliquot is diluted to approximately 100 ml., and 20 ml. of concentrated nitric acid is added. The solution is boiled for 20 to 30 minutes to hydrolyze the poly- and metaphosphates to orthophosphate. After cooling, the solution is neutralized to methyl orange with ammonium hydroxide and is again cooled to room temperature. Phosphate is precipitated as ammonium 12-molybdophosphate, filtered, washed, and titrated by the volumetric procedure recommended for fertilizers.[18]*

References

1. AUDRIETH and HILL: *J. Chem. Education,* **25,** 80 (1948).
2. HILL: thesis, University of Illinois, 1948.
3. AUDRIETH and MOELLER: *J. Chem. Education,* **20,** 219 (1943).
4. VAN WAZER: private communication.
5. KARBE and JANDER: *Kolloid-Beihefte,* **54,** 1 (1942).
6. MALGREN and LAMM: *Z. anorg. allgem. Chem.,* **245,** 103 (1940); **252,** 256 (1944).
7. WEINBERG: thesis, University of Illinois, 1947.
8. WALBROTH: *Bull. soc. chim.,* (2) **39,** 316 (1883).
9. COHN: *Chem. News,* **129,** 32 (1934).
10. ZINTL and BERTRAM: *Z. anorg. allgem. Chem.,* **245,** 16 (1940).
11. BELL: *Ind. Eng. Chem.,* **39,** 136 (1947).
12. WEBER and KING: INORGANIC SYNTHESIS, **1,** 101 (1939).
13. BELL: *Ind. Eng. Chem.,* **40,** 1464 (1948).
14. FISKE and SUBBAROW: *J. Biol. Chem.,* **66,** 375 (1925).
15. BELL and DOISY: *ibid.,* **44,** 55 (1920).
16. BELL: *Anal. Chem.,* **19,** 97 (1947).
17. JONES: *Anal. Chem.,* **14,** 536 (1942).
18. "Methods of Analysis of Official Association of Agricultural Chemists," 6th ed. pp. 22–3, George Banta Publishing Company (The Collegiate Press), Menasha, Wis., 1945.

* No satisfactory method has yet been worked out for the direct determination of trimetaphosphate. The difference between (1) the total water-soluble P_2O_5 content and (2) the sum of that calculated for each of the phosphates is usually ascribed to the trimetaphosphate content and calculated as such. If this amounts to an appreciable percentage, its presence can be verified by adding 1 g. of sodium hydroxide to a 50-ml. aliquot of the sample solution, boiling for 5 minutes, and redetermining the triphosphate content. When treated in this manner, trimetaphosphate is converted to triphosphate in accordance with the following equation: $(NaPO_3)_3 + 2NaOH \rightarrow Na_5P_3O_{10} + H_2O$. Any increase in the triphosphate content is calculated to trimetaphosphate. Although this is not an exact procedure, it does verify the presence of trimetaphosphate and gives an estimate of the amount present.

23. PYROPHOSPHORIC ACID

(Diphosphoric Acid)

SUBMITTED BY J. E. MALOWAN*
CHECKED BY R. N. BELL†

Solid pyrophosphoric acid is obtainable only by the spontaneous crystallization of a polyphosphoric acid mixture containing 79.8 ± 0.2 per cent phosphorus(V) oxide. Such a liquid polyphosphoric acid may be prepared (1) by dehydration of 85 per cent orthophosphoric acid, (2) by dissolving phosphorus(V) oxide in 85 per cent orthophosphoric acid, (3) by adding water to commercial "tetraphosphoric acid," or (4) by allowing phosphorus(V) oxychloride to react with 85 per cent phosphoric acid. The first three of these procedures are preferred.

Procedure

A liquid polyphosphoric acid containing approximately 80 per cent phosphorus(V) oxide is first prepared by one of the methods described below. After analysis, its composition is adjusted by addition of water to give a product containing 79.8 per cent phosphorus(V) oxide [theoretical for pyrophosphoric acid, 79.76 per cent phosphorus(V) oxide].

A. CONCENTRATION OF
85 PER CENT ORTHOPHOSPHORIC ACID

The commercially available 85 per cent orthophosphoric acid is concentrated by heating in an oil bath (or by using a Glas-col heater) to prevent local overheating and under vacuum to reduce the required temperature. Concentration is continued until loss in weight amounts to 25 to 30 g. per 100 g. of 85 per cent orthophosphoric acid (theory 22.81 per cent). It will generally be necessary to continue

* Monsanto Chemical Company, Central Research Dept., Dayton, Ohio.
† Victor Chemical Works Research Laboratory, Chicago Heights, Ill.

heating until the temperature of the liquid acid has reached approximately 180°.

B. SOLUTION OF PHOSPHORUS(V) OXIDE IN 85 PER CENT ORTHOPHOSPHORIC ACID

The required quantity of phosphorus(V) oxide is added slowly and in small portions (3 to 5 g. at a time) to the acid in a two-necked, round-bottomed flask equipped with a motor-driven stirrer. The solution of the oxide proceeds slowly, and vigorous agitation together with application of heat is required to obtain a clear solution. Approximately 95 to 100 g. of phosphorus(V) oxide should be added for each 100 g. of 85 per cent orthophosphoric acid.

C. DILUTION OF TETRAPHOSPHORIC ACID

Commercial tetraphosphoric acid contains about 82.5 per cent phosphorus(V) oxide (theory, 84 per cent). Three grams of water or 12 g. of 85 per cent orthophosphoric acid should be added for each 100-g. portion of the acid. The water or acid is added slowly with agitation. Stirring will be difficult at first because of the very high viscosity of the starting material, but the heat of dilution will serve to decrease the viscosity rapidly.

The total phosphorus(V) oxide content of the product, prepared by one of the above procedures, is then determined[4] (synthesis 22) and the composition adjusted to 79.76 per cent phosphorus(V) oxide by the addition of water. The acid is allowed to crystallize spontaneously. If the solution is permitted to stand at room temperature, it may be two weeks or longer before solidification is complete. If the solution is kept in an ice chest, crystallization will usually occur within a few days to form a hard cake containing 85 to 95 per cent pyrophosphoric acid[5,6] together with occluded mother liquor consisting largely of a mixture of ortho-, meta- and triphosphoric acids. During crystallization a slight increase in volume takes place and may result in the rupture of the glass container. It is therefore advisable to use a comparatively large bottle or a stainless-steel or lead vessel. The product is very hygroscopic and must be stored in a closed container.

Properties

Pure pyrophosphoric acid exists in the solid form, or dissolved in various inert solvents. When heated above its melting point (61°), it decomposes into a liquid mixture consisting of ortho-, pyro-, tri-, and polymetaphosphoric acids.[1,2] The crystalline acid may be dissolved in ice water to give a solution that will remain unchanged for some time. When the compound is dissolved in water at higher temperatures, hydration occurs to give increasing amounts of orthophosphoric acid. Molecular-weight determinations indicate that pyrophosphoric acid exhibits some tendency to form polymeric aggregates of compositions up to $(H_4P_2O_7)_5$. Solution in glacial acetic acid or in water appears to effect slow depolymerization.[3]

References

1. LUM, MALOWAN, and DURGIN: *Chem. & Met. Eng.*, **44**, 721 (1937).
2. BELL, *Ind. Eng. Chem.*, **39**, 136 (1947).
3. HOLT and MYERS: *J. Chem. Soc.*, **99**, 384 (1911).
4. "Methods of Analysis of the Association of Official Agricultural Chemists," 6th ed., p. 22, George Banta Publishing Company (The Collegiate Press), Menasha, Wis., 1945.
5. BRITSKE and DRAGUNOW: *J. Chem. Ind. (U.S.S.R.)*, **4**, 49 (1927).
6. BELL: *Anal. Chem.*, **19**, 97 (1947).

24. SODIUM PYROPHOSPHATES

(Sodium Diphosphates)

SUBMITTED BY R. N. BELL*
CHECKED BY W. L. JOLLY† AND L. F. AUDRIETH†

The sodium pyrophosphates are the first products formed in the dehydration (aggregation) of the sodium orthophosphates. Careful thermal treatment of sodium dihydrogen

* Victor Chemical Works Research Laboratory, Chicago Heights, Ill.
† University of Illinois, Urbana, Ill.

orthophosphate leads to the dihydrogen pyrophosphate as an intermediate. Complete thermal dehydration of disodium hydrogen orthophosphate yields the tetrasodium pyrophosphate. An alternative method of preparing the dihydrogen pyrophosphate by crystallization from strong acetic acid solution is also presented.

Procedure

A. DISODIUM DIHYDROGEN PYROPHOSPHATE

$$2NaH_2PO_4 \xrightarrow{\Delta} Na_2H_2P_2O_7 + H_2O$$
$$Na_4P_2O_7 + 2HC_2H_3O_2 \rightarrow Na_2H_2P_2O_7 + 2NaC_2H_3O_2$$

Pure sodium dihydrogen orthophosphate, NaH_2PO_4, when heated to 210° for 12 hours, gives a product that will analyze over 97 per cent as $Na_2H_2P_2O_7$ by the methods of Britske and Dragunov[1] or of Bell.[2] Recrystallization of the orthophosphate and drying at 70° before converting to the pyrophosphate is recommended. When prepared in this manner the crystals are too small for optical measurements. Larger crystals are produced by the following alternative method.

To 100 ml. of a saturated aqueous solution of tetrasodium pyrophosphate at 40° there is added 75 ml. of glacial acetic acid. After the acetic acid has been added, the temperature is brought back up to 40° and the solution agitated until crystallization is complete (approx. 2 to 3 hours). Crystals will appear in 30 to 60 minutes and grow slowly. When crystallization has proceeded for about 30 minutes, the temperature may be dropped slowly to 30°, but not less.* The crystals are filtered off using vacuum, washed with two portions of ice water, and dried at 100°. This procedure yields about 5 g. of anhydrous crystals which, if grown slowly enough, are of sufficient size for study under a microscope.

* At lower temperatures, a mixture of anhydrous and hydrated crystals, $Na_2H_2P_2O_7 \cdot 6H_2O$, is obtained. Below 20°, the hydrate predominates.

B. TETRASODIUM PYROPHOSPHATE

$$2Na_2HPO_4 \rightarrow Na_4P_2O_7 + H_2O$$

Tetrasodium pyrophosphate is formed when pure disodium hydrogen orthophosphate is heated to 500° for 5 hours. The product will contain better than 98 per cent $Na_4P_2O_7$. Crystalline masses large enough for optical measurements are produced by heating in platinum to above the melting point of the tetrasodium pyrophosphate, 800°, and cooling slowly. Higher temperatures or longer heating times do not change the tetrasodium pyrophosphate, as this is the final product in the dehydration of disodium hydrogen orthophosphate.

Properties

Disodium dihydrogen pyrophosphate dissolves slowly in cold water, a 1 per cent solution having a pH of 4.1 to 4.3. One hydrate, $Na_2H_2P_2O_7 \cdot 6H_2O$, can be crystallized from aqueous solutions at slightly below room temperature. The hydrated crystals are biaxial negative with $\alpha = 1.456$, $\beta = 1.464$, and $\gamma = 1.465(\pm .002)$. When heated they lose their water of crystallization around 36°. In aqueous solution the disodium pyrophosphate hydrolyzes to orthophosphate, the rate of hydrolysis depending on the temperature. At 70° a 1 per cent solution is hydrolyzed approximately 10 per cent in 6 hours; at 100° the hydrolysis is complete in less than 6 hours.[3]

When anhydrous disodium dihydrogen pyrophosphate is prepared by the acetic acid method, the product is sufficiently crystalline for optical measurements. The crystals are orthorhombic pyramids, biaxial negative with $\alpha = 1.501 \pm .002, \beta = 1.514 \pm .005$, and $\gamma = 1.522 \pm .002$. Ingerson and Morey[4] give $\alpha' = 1.510$ and $\gamma' = 1.517$ for very fine needle crystals.

Tetrasodium pyrophosphate is quite soluble in cold water; a 1 per cent solution has a pH of 10.2. It hydrolyzes to orthophosphate in aqueous solution but the rate of hydrolysis is much slower than for the more acid pyrophosphate. No noticeable hydrolysis takes place in 60 hours at 70°.[3] One hydrate is known, $Na_4P_2O_7 \cdot 10H_2O$, that can be crystallized from aqueous solution below 79°. The hydrate melts at 79.5° but is efflorescent at temperatures slightly below the melting point. A fairly accurate melting-point determination can be made with the hot-stage microscope by mounting the crystals in an inert liquid such as mineral oil. The hydrated crystals are biaxial positive with $\alpha = 1.450$, $\beta = 1.453$, and $\gamma = 1.460$ ($\pm.002$). Anhydrous tetrasodium pyrophosphate is biaxial positive with $\alpha = 1.475$, $\beta = 1.477$, and $\gamma = 1.496$ ($\pm.002$).

References

1. BRITSKE and DRAGUNOV: *J. Chem. Ind. (U.S.S.R.)*, **4**, 49 (1927).
2. BELL: *Anal. Chem.*, **19**, 97 (1947).
3. BELL: *Ind. Eng. Chem.*, **39**, 136 (1947).
4. INGERSON and MOREY: *Am. Mineral.*, **28**, 448 (1943).

25. SODIUM TRIPHOSPHATE

(Sodium Tripolyphosphate)

$$2Na_2HPO_4 + NaH_2PO_4 \xrightarrow{\Delta} Na_5P_3O_{10} + 2H_2O$$

SUBMITTED BY R. N. BELL*
CHECKED BY W. L. JOLLY† AND L. F. AUDRIETH†

Sodium triphosphate (more frequently called tripolyphosphate), $Na_5P_3O_{10}$, occurs in two forms, which are usually designated as types I and II. By varying the technique of heating, either type can be made from a mixture consisting of (1) 2 mols of a sodium phosphate having a sodium-to-phosphorus ratio of 2:1, and (2) 1 mol of a phosphate having a 1:1 sodium-to-phosphorus ratio. The phosphate mixture can be prepared either by mixing intimately the finely powdered dry salts or by evaporating to dryness a solution containing Na_2O and P_2O_5 in the proper molar ratio, 5:3. The use of orthophosphates is recommended

* Victor Chemical Works Research Laboratory, Chicago Heights, Ill.
† University of Illinois, Urbana, Ill.

since these are most easily obtained pure or can be purified readily by recrystallization. Triphosphate is also obtained by treating a solution of the trimetaphosphate with strong caustic solution.[4]

Procedure

Sodium triphosphate I, the stable phase, is produced when an intimate mixture of 1 mol of sodium dihydrogen orthophosphate with 2 mols of disodium hydrogen orthophosphate is heated to 540 to 580° for 2 hours in a platinum dish.*

Sodium triphosphate II, the metastable phase, is produced by heating this same orthophosphate mixture in a platinum dish to well above the dissociation temperature of sodium triphosphate, 620°, until a clear melt is obtained. Temperatures between 850 and 900° will be required. After this stage has been attained, the temperature is dropped to 550° where the product is annealed for at least 2 hours.† The material is then removed from the muffle and allowed to cool rapidly in air. At a temperature between 150 and 100° the solid undergoes a crystalline phase transition with disintegration into a powder. This phenomenon is characteristic of type II but not of type I.

Properties

The two types of sodium triphosphate are most readily distinguished by their x-ray diffraction patterns.[1] The refractive indexes of the two types are too nearly alike to make possible identification by this means as both fall within the following limits:

$$\alpha = 1.473 \pm .004$$
$$\beta = 1.478 \pm .002$$
and $$\gamma = 1.503 \pm .002$$

Type II sodium triphosphate is relatively stable below 450°,

---

* Actual quantities are not given, since several hydrates of both Na_2HPO_4 and NaH_2PO_4 are available; in making the original reaction mixture the composition of these hydrates must be taken into account.

† If the product is cooled rapidly from a melt, a glass is obtained.

but changes to type I if reheated to between 500 and 600°. Both types dissociate above 620° to give a melt containing crystals of pyrophosphate in molten polymetaphosphate.

Both types are soluble in water, the metastable phase dissolving more rapidly and readily. A 1 per cent solution has a pH of 9.7. Triphosphate hydrolyzes in aqueous solution to 1 mol each of pyrophosphate and orthophosphate, the rate of hydrolysis depending on the temperature. Approximately 50 per cent is hydrolyzed in 6 hours at 100°, while only 15 per cent is hydrolyzed in 60 hours at 70°.[2]

One hydrate, $Na_5P_3O_{10} \cdot 6H_2O$, is known; it can be precipitated from a concentrated aqueous solution of either type I or II by saturating with sodium chloride. The 6-hydrate decomposes without melting around 120°. It is almost entirely reconverted into anhydrous triphosphate by heating for 5 hours at 320°. The crystals of the hydrate are flat rectangular plates, biaxial positive with $\alpha = 1.450$, $\beta = 1.452$, and $\gamma = 1.480$ (+.002). The indexes for the normal view are $\alpha' = 1.450$ and $\gamma' = 1.470$. Although no exact method of analysis for triphosphate has been reported, a fairly accurate estimate of the quantity present can be obtained by a modified Britske-Dragunov titration.[3]

References

1. PARTRIDGE, HICKS, and SMITH: *J. Am. Chem. Soc.*, **63**, 454 (1941).
2. BELL: *Ind. Eng. Chem.*, **39**, 136 (1947).
3. BELL: *Anal. Chem.*, **19**, 97 (1947).
4. HATCH: U.S. patent 2365190 (December 19, 1944); *cf. Chem. Abstracts*, **39**, 4508 (1945).

26. SODIUM METAPHOSPHATES

$$xNaH_2PO_4 \xrightarrow{\Delta} (NaPO_3)_x + xH_2O$$

SUBMITTED BY R. N. BELL*
CHECKED BY W. L. JOLLY† AND L. F. AUDRIETH†

The sodium metaphosphates are the final products in the dehydration (aggregation) of sodium dihydrogen ortho-

* Victor Chemical Works Research Laboratory, Chicago Heights, Ill.
† University of Illinois, Urbana, Ill.

phosphate.   Several polymeric forms may be prepared by varying the thermal treatment.   Of these, the trimetaphosphate containing the $P_3O_9{}^{3-}$ grouping is the best known; it is sometimes referred to as the monometaphosphate, or as $NaPO_3$ I.

Sodium polymetaphosphate (Graham's salt), usually but improperly termed "hexametaphosphate," is the most useful of the metaphosphates owing to its ability to "sequester" calcium ions.   Graham's salt is the end member of a series of sodium phosphate glasses that dissolve in water to give solutions containing polyanionic metaphosphate complexes whose ionic weights have been shown to be of the order to 10,000[1,2] and higher.   There is no justification whatsoever for the name hexametaphosphate.

Procedure

A. SODIUM TRIMETAPHOSPHATE

Sodium trimetaphosphate can be prepared by (1) heating sodium dihydrogen orthophosphate for 5 hours at 530° or (2) tempering a glassy sodium metaphosphate at 520° for 12 hours.   If the product obtained by the first of these procedures is not entirely water-soluble, additional heating will be necessary to eliminate the insoluble polymer that forms at a lower temperature.

The 6-hydrate, $Na_3P_3O_9 \cdot 6H_2O$, is prepared in the following manner: Fifty-one grams (0.166 mol) of anhydrous sodium trimetaphosphate is dissolved in 160 ml. of water at room temperature.   Forty-five milliliters of a saturated solution of sodium chloride is added and the mixture agitated for 4 hours.   The crystalline product, amounting to 23 g. (33 per cent of theory), is filtered and dried in air.

B. SODIUM POLYMETAPHOSPHATE (GRAHAM'S SALT)
$(NaPO_3)_x$

The glass obtained by rapidly chilling a sodium metaphosphate melt is the highly polymerized polymetaphosphate.   It can be prepared by heating any sodium phosphate having a 1:1 sodium-to-phosphorus ratio until it forms a clear melt and then chilling rapidly. Sodium dihydrogen orthophosphate, disodium dihydrogen pyrophosphate, or a lower polymer of sodium metaphosphate is heated in platinum to 700 to 900° until a clear melt is obtained. This melt is then poured onto a steel plate and covered with a second steel plate in order to effect rapid chilling and to prevent reversion to lower polymers. The glassy "buttons" usually shatter as they cool, so care should be taken to prevent loss of the material or injury to workers. A cloth held lightly around the edge of the plates while the button is cooling will provide sufficient protection. If the product does not disintegrate while cooling, the button should be covered with a cloth and tapped lightly.

Properties

Anhydrous sodium trimetaphosphate is crystalline and water-soluble, but has no calcium-sequestering value. The trimetaphosphate is not precipitated by zinc, silver, or barium ions.[3] Slow hydrolysis occurs in aqueous solution to give orthophosphate ions with intermediate formation of triphosphate ions. Conversion to triphosphate occurs very rapidly when the trimetaphosphate is heated for a few minutes at 100° in the presence of an excess of sodium hydroxide. No satisfactory quantitative method for its determination has been reported. It can, however, be identified by its refractive indexes, since the crystals are biaxial negative with $\alpha = 1.471$, $\beta = 1.476$, $\gamma = 1.480$ ($\pm.002$).

Crystals of the 6-hydrate, $Na_3P_3O_9 \cdot 6H_2O$, are triclinic rhombohedra, biaxial negative with $\alpha = 1.433$, $\beta = 1.442$, and $\gamma = 1.446$ ($\pm.002$). These crystals are efflorescent at room temperature, lose water rapidly at 50°, and melt in their water of crystallization if heated rapidly to around 53°.

Sodium polymetaphosphate (Graham's salt) is a clear

glass having a refractive index of 1.482 ± .002. It has not been found possible to produce a glass that will analyze over 92 to 95 per cent polymetaphosphate using the method of analysis devised by Jones,[4] although this procedure has been found to be the most satisfactory for the determination of the so-called "hexametaphosphate."

Sodium polymetaphosphate dissolves slowly in water, but is very soluble. A 1 per cent solution has a pH of about 6.2. In aqueous solutions it depolymerizes to the trimetaphosphate and hydrolyzes to orthophosphate.[3] Both reactions take place simultaneously, the rates depending largely on the temperature.

References

1. LAMM: *Arkiv Kemi, Mineral. Geol.*, **17A**, No. 25, 27 pp. (1944).
2. SAMUELSON: *Svensk Kem. Tid.*, **56**, 343 (1944).
3. BELL: *Ind. Eng. Chem.*, **39**, 136 (1947).
4. JONES: *Anal. Chem.*, **14**, 536 (1942).

27. SODIUM MONOFLUOPHOSPHATE

$$Na_3P_3O_9 + 3NaF \rightarrow 3Na_2PO_3F$$

SUBMITTED BY O. F. HILL* AND L. F. AUDRIETH*
CHECKED BY R. N. BELL†

Sodium monofluophosphate has been prepared (1) by treating silver monofluophosphate with the stoichiometric amounts of sodium chloride,[1] (2) by treating ammonium monofluophosphate with the stoichiometric amount of sodium hydroxide,[2] and (3) by neutralizing a solution of monofluophosphoric acid.[3] It is difficult to prepare a pure product in good yields by these procedures. Furthermore, it is necessary to handle relatively large volumes of solutions when these methods are employed, and these solutions must then be concentrated at low temperatures and at reduced pressures in order to prevent hydrolysis. The procedure outlined here gives a pure product in excellent

* University of Illinois, Urbana, Ill.
† Victor Chemical Works Research Laboratory, Chicago Heights, Ill.

yields with a minimum of manipulation. The crude product, obtained initially in the fusion reaction, is satisfactory for most purposes.

Procedure

An intimate mixture of 40 g. of anhydrous sodium trimetaphosphate* and 16.48 g. of anhydrous sodium fluoride is placed in a 100-ml. platinum dish. The dish and its contents are then placed in a muffle furnace at 800° for about 6 minutes, no more than long enough to effect complete fusion of the mixture. The fused mass is removed from the furnace, allowed to cool to below red heat in the open air, and then cooled to room temperature in a desiccator. This product consists of about 90 per cent sodium monofluophosphate. A small weight loss (0.2 to 0.3 per cent), due to the decomposition of sodium monofluophosphate, accompanies the fusion reaction.

To purify the crude product the cooled mass is ground in a mortar and dissolved in 200 ml. of distilled water. The heat of solution will cause the temperature of the solution to rise a few degrees, but not enough to cause any appreciable hydrolysis of the monofluophosphate. Any insoluble material is filtered off since it consists mainly of sodium pyrophosphate. Solid silver monofluophosphate (synthesis 28) (about 1 g.) is then added to the solution (or the filtrate). After stirring for 10 to 15 minutes, the solution is tested for complete removal of pyrophosphate by adding silver nitrate solution to a diluted portion of the supernatant of a centrifuged or filtered sample. If precipitation does occur, it is necessary to add more silver monofluophosphate. The insoluble silver salts are removed by filtration and the filtrate is treated with a slight excess of 10 per cent sodium hydroxide solution to remove the excess silver ions. After stirring for a few minutes to coagulate

* $Na_3P_3O_9$ is the metaphosphate chosen for this fusion reaction since it may be prepared readily in the anhydrous state. Other sodium metaphosphates, such as Graham's salt, may also be employed, but even small amounts of moisture will bring about some hydrolysis of the monofluophosphate with a resulting decrease in the yield.

the silver oxide that precipitates, the solution is again filtered.

The filtrate, containing sodium monofluophosphate and a small amount of sodium hydroxide, is treated with an equal volume of ethyl alcohol. After thorough agitation, the mixture is allowed to separate into two layers. The alcoholic layer, containing some of the water of the original solution, is decanted and rejected. The aqueous portion is again treated with an equal volume of alcohol and the process repeated. On the second or third extraction, sodium monofluophosphate starts to crystallize in small crystallites. These crystals form in the aqueous layer, which is now only a fraction of the original volume, and give to the thick viscous solution the appearance of a white oil. The alcoholic extraction and decantation process is continued until the crystals of sodium monofluophosphate settle readily and only one liquid phase is present. This extraction procedure removes all the water and sodium hydroxide to yield an anhydrous product. The crystals are filtered, washed on the funnel with ether, and air-dried. The yield of sodium monofluophosphate is 45.7 g. (81.1 per cent).

To analyze the product for phosphorus and fluorine, the latter is first distilled as hexafluosilicic acid in the presence of perchloric acid.[4] The fluorine content of the distillate is then determined by titrating with standard thorium nitrate solution at a pH of about 3, using sodium alizarinsulfonate as the indicator.[5] The phosphorus may be determined in the residue remaining after distillation by precipitating ammonium 12-molybdophosphate, dissolving the precipitate in an excess of standard sodium hydroxide, and titrating the excess base with standard acid.[6] *Anal.* Calcd. for Na_2PO_3F: F, 13.19; P, 21.53. Found: F, 13.17; P, 21.53.

Properties

For a general statement of the properties of monofluophosphates, see Lange, INORGANIC SYNTHESES, **2,** 156 (1946).

Sodium monofluophosphate is very soluble in water. The heat of solution is large enough to cause a temperature rise when a concentrated solution is prepared. The solution is neutral and fairly stable at room temperature, but does undergo slow hydrolysis to orthophosphate and fluoride. Hydrolysis takes place rapidly in acid solution.

Sodium monofluophosphate undergoes thermal decomposition at higher temperatures, yielding pyrophosphate. In a wet atmosphere the decomposition takes place through the evolution of hydrogen fluoride.

The potassium salt may be prepared in a like fashion by fusing potassium metaphosphate and potassium fluoride.

References

1. LANGE: *Ber.*, **62B**, 793 (1929).
2. MARQUINA: *Rev. acad. cienc. exact. físquím. y nat. Madrid*, **30**, 382 (1933).
3. LANGE and LIVINGSTON: *J. Am. Chem. Soc.*, **69**, 1073 (1947).
4. WILLARD and WINTER: *Anal. Chem.*, **5**, 7 (1933).
4. ROWLEY and CHURCHILL: *ibid.*, **9**, 551 (1937).
6. "Methods of Analysis of the Association of Official Agricultural Chemists," 6th ed., p. 22, George Banta Publishing Company (The Collegiate Press), Menasha, Wis., 1945.

28. SILVER MONOFLUOPHOSPHATE

$$Na_2PO_3F + 2AgNO_3 \rightarrow Ag_2PO_3F + 2NaNO_3$$

SUBMITTED BY L. F. AUDRIETH* AND O. F. HILL*
CHECKED BY R. N. BELL†

Silver monofluophosphate is needed in the purification of crude sodium monofluophosphate. It has been prepared by Lange from the ammonium fluoride–phosphorus(V) oxide fusion residues[1,2] but, using the same general technique, it is more conveniently made from a sodium metaphosphate–sodium fluoride fusion residue. The impurities in such a mixture are the various phosphates whose silver salts are quite insoluble and may be removed from solution as such; silver monofluophosphate is prepared by adding solid silver nitrate to the filtrate.

* University of Illinois, Urbana, Ill.
† Victor Chemical Works Research Laboratory, Chicago Heights, Ill.

Procedure

A sodium metaphosphate–sodium fluoride fusion residue is prepared in accordance with the directions for the preparation of sodium monofluophosphate (synthesis 27). The fused mass (about 55 g.) is powdered in a mortar and dissolved in 200 ml. of distilled water. Any insoluble material is filtered off and rejected. A slight excess of 10 per cent aqueous silver nitrate is added to the solution (or the filtrate). The insoluble silver salts are removed by filtration when a test* of a diluted portion indicates that an excess of silver ion has been added. Solid silver nitrate is then added to the filtrate to near the point of saturation. Silver monofluophosphate forms as finely divided crystals. These are filtered off on a Büchner funnel and washed with cold water. The filtrate and washings may be treated with additional solid silver nitrate to increase the yield. The precipitate is first air-dried on a Büchner funnel and then dried further by pressing between sheets of filter paper. The resulting crystals are then dried completely *in vacuo* over phosphorus(V) oxide. Since exposure to light causes decomposition, the vacuum drying should be carried out in the dark. In a typical experiment a yield of 77.2 g. (62.8 per cent) was obtained. *Anal.* Calcd. for Ag_2PO_3F: F, 6.06; P, 9.88. Found: F, 5.98; P, 9.93.

Properties

Silver monofluophosphate forms the anhydrous salt. It is sparingly soluble in water; according to Lange, the solubility is 5.93×10^{-2} mol per liter at 20°. Like all monofluophosphates, it undergoes slow hydrolysis to orthophos-

---

* The reagent is added to the supernatant of a diluted portion of a centrifuged or filtered sample. Addition of the silver nitrate solution to the concentrated solution is apt to be misleading since silver monofluophosphate has a limited solubility.

phate and fluoride in contact with water; hydrolysis is more rapid in acid solution.

References

1. LANGE: *Ber.*, **62B**, 793 (1929).
2. LANGE: INORGANIC SYNTHESES, **2**, 155 (1946).

29. HEXAFLUOPHOSPHATES OF SODIUM, AMMONIUM, AND POTASSIUM

$$MCl + PCl_5 + 6HF \rightarrow MPF_6 + 6HCl \text{ (in liquid HF)}$$

SUBMITTED BY M. M. WOYSKI[*]
CHECKED BY W. J. SHENK, JR.,[†] AND E. R. PELLON[†]

Two methods are available for the preparation of hexafluophosphates. The method developed by Lange and Krueger[3] employs the reaction of phosphorus(V) chloride with alkali metal fluorides or ammonium fluoride as indicated by the type equation

$$PCl_5 + 6MF \rightarrow MPF_6 + 5MCl.$$

Separation of the hexafluophosphate from the large amount of metal chloride is effected by precipitation of the former with nitron acetate, treatment of the resulting precipitate with aqueous ammonia, extraction of the liberated nitron with chloroform, and crystallization in the case of the ammonium salt or direct fractional crystallization in the case of the potassium salt. Only small quantities of the sodium, potassium, and ammonium salts have been obtained by this procedure.

The second method, described below, can be employed for the preparation of any desired quantity of substantially pure material. It involves fluorination of both the metal and phosphorus(V) chlorides in liquid hydrogen fluoride and subsequent interaction of the products in this medium.

* University of Illinois, Urbana, Ill.
† Harshaw Chemical Company, Cleveland 6, Ohio.

Since anhydrous hydrogen fluoride serves as the reaction medium, special equipment is needed. An efficient fume hood is absolutely necessary. Care must be exercised in the handling of hydrogen fluoride to avoid injury to the operator.

CAUTION!

Anhydrous hydrogen fluoride must be handled with the greatest care. Avoid contact with either the liquid or the vapor. A droplet of the liquid on the skin produces a severe burn almost instantly. Vapor condensed on the skin is absorbed and produces painful and serious aftereffects. The handling of anhydrous hydrogen fluoride in open vessels should not be undertaken, except in a very efficient fume hood, and only after careful consideration of the procedure to be followed.

In case of accident it is essential that the affected spots be rinsed and soaked first with copious quantities of water, then with dilute aqueous ammonia, and subsequently be treated by alternate rinsing with water and soaking in ammonium carbonate solution. A poultice of magnesium hydroxide (20 per cent by weight in glycerol) may be applied. An antiseptic and a local anesthetic are frequently incorporated in this mixture. A 10 per cent solution of calcium gluconate may be injected around the area. Neglected burns swell, become extremely painful and must usually be lanced, and even then heal very slowly.

It is advisable to be prepared for emergencies whenever hydrogen fluoride is to be employed. Since physicians are not generally familiar with the treatment of hydrogen fluoride burns, it is further suggested that the operator avail himself of the most recent information on this subject.

Procedure

The reaction is carried out in a stainless-steel, nickel or Monel vessel, 3 in. in diameter and 7 in. high, which is fitted with a cover and connecting tubes as shown in Fig.

20.* One-half mol† of the desired chloride‡ is placed in the vessel, the cover is attached, and the vessel is chilled in an ice-salt bath. Connection is made with a cylinder

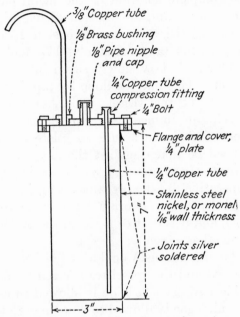

FIG. 20. Diagram of all-metal container for carrying out reactions in liquid anhydrous hydrogen fluoride.

of anhydrous hydrogen fluoride; the valve is opened, and approximately 400 ml. of the liquid is allowed to condense in the vessel. This will fill the stainless-steel vessel to a depth of about $3\frac{3}{4}$ in. The depth may be gaged by insert-

* This is the simplest practical apparatus. If this synthesis is used extensively it is worthwhile to construct a jacketed reaction vessel that can be cooled with circulating brine. The use of a screw feed device attached to the cover, and a mechanical stirrer, also adds to the safety and convenience of the operation.

† This procedure has been found to give satisfactory results when carried out in batches of six times this size in a proportionally larger reaction vessel. Such large-scale operation is hazardous unless the more elaborate equipment suggested in the previous footnote is used.

‡ Fluorides may be used, but chlorides are recommended for convenience.

ing a thin wooden splint through the central tube. That portion of the wooden splint immersed in the liquid will be charred.

To ensure complete solution of the metal chloride the cover is then removed and the solution stirred using a stainless-steel spoon fitted with an extension handle. One hundred fifty grams (approximately 0.75 mol) of phosphorus(V) chloride is now slowly sifted into the solution from the spoon. This may be done by tapping the spoon against the side of the vessel. The hexafluophosphate begins to precipitate immediately, but the solution should be stirred occasionally to assure complete reaction. No precaution need be taken against the entrance of atmospheric moisture. Inasmuch as the reaction is rather vigorous, it is imperative to take precautions against spattering of the liquid hydrogen fluoride. Heavy rubber gloves must be worn, and it is best to perform the operation from behind a protective screen.

After all the phosphorus(V) chloride has been added, the cover is replaced and the vessel transferred to an oil bath. The remaining hydrogen fluoride is allowed to escape. A stream of dry nitrogen is allowed to flow through the vessel, which is then heated to about 150° to remove the last traces of hydrogen fluoride.

Yields are substantially theoretical, with a purity well in excess of 95 per cent. The product is contaminated by traces of iron salts and sometimes by small quantities of unreacted metal fluoride.

Purification

Ammonium Salt. The crude product weighing about 80 g. is dissolved in 160 ml. methanol. A few drops of water and an excess of ammonia (in methanol) are added to precipitate the iron impurities. The solution is filtered and evaporated to dryness in a vacuum desiccator. The product is dehydrated over sulfuric acid. The yield, based on the ammonium chloride employed, is 70 g. (86 per cent).

Anal. Calcd. for NH_4PF_6: N, 8.60; P, 19.0; F, 69.9. Found: N, 8.45; P, 19.4; F, 69.5.

The salt so purified may contain some ammonium fluoride, which can be removed only by recrystallization of the product from water. This is a wasteful process due to the great solubility of the fluophosphate. The salt is dissolved in water (50 g./100 ml.) and the filtered solution evaporated in a platinum dish on a steam bath until crystals appear in the hot solution. The mixture is chilled in ice, and the crystals are collected on a sintered-glass suction filter, washed with a few milliliters of ice water, sucked free from adhering moisture, and dried in a desiccator over sulfuric acid.

Sodium Salt. The crude salt is dissolved in methanol, using 100 ml. of solvent for each 60 g. of product. A 5 per cent solution of sodium hydroxide in methanol is added in just sufficient amount to render the solution permanently alkaline, as indicated by spot tests with phenolphthalein. Since difficulty may be experienced in filtering the basic solution, it is recommended that impurities be separated from the alcoholic solution by centrifugation. The solvent is removed by concentration and crystallization under reduced pressure to yield a product consisting of the monohydrate, which on drying over sulfuric acid is converted into the anhydrous salt. Yield of purified product from 0.5 mol sodium chloride is 73 g. (87 per cent).

Potassium Salt. The potassium salt is much less soluble in cold water than either of the preceding salts (about 8 g./100 ml.). Moreover, the temperature coefficient of solubility is large. The salt is easily purified, therefore, by recrystallization from water. The crude product, weighing about 90 g., is dissolved in 225 ml. of hot water. Potassium hydroxide solution is added until the solution is alkaline to phenolphthalein, to precipitate metallic impurities. The solution is digested for ½ hour on the steam bath and filtered through a Büchner funnel that has been heated to 125° in an oven. The hot solution is transferred to a beaker and is then chilled thoroughly in an ice bath. The crystals are collected on a sintered-glass suction filter, washed with two 10-ml. portions of ice water, and dried over sulfuric acid. The recovery is about 67 g. (73 per cent). Several grams of less pure product may be obtained by evaporating the solution in a platinum dish on the steam bath until crystals appear. *Anal.* Calcd. for KPF_6: P, 16.8; F, 62.0.   Found: P, 17.0; F, 61.7.

Storage

The hexafluophosphates may be stored in glass for indefinite periods if moisture is rigorously excluded. The ammonium salt is easily dehydrated over sulfuric acid and keeps well. Greater care must be taken with the sodium salt, which in the form of the monohydrate loses water only slowly over anhydrous calcium chloride. To prevent contamination, storage in waxed bottles, after dehydration over sulfuric acid, is recommended.

Properties

The properties of the hexafluophosphates have been investigated by Lange and coworkers.[1-4] The salts of hexafluophosphoric acid generally show solubility characteristics very similar to those of the perchlorates.[2] The sodium and ammonium salts are very soluble in water. The solubilities of some other salts, in mols per liter at room temperature, are as follows:

KPF_6	0.432	$Ni(NH_3)_6(PF_6)_2$	0.0077
$RbPF_6$	0.076	$(CH_3)_4NPF_6$	0.0077
$CsPF_6$	0.030	$C_{20}H_{16}N_4 \cdot HPF_6$*	0.0002

The nitron salt may be used for the quantitative estimation of the hexafluophosphate ion according to the procedure of Lange and Müller.[2] The ammonium and sodium salts are also soluble in methanol, ethanol, acetone, and methyl acetate.

* Nitron hexafluophosphate.

The hexafluophosphates are remarkably stable toward hydrolysis. No significant hydrolysis takes place in the cold in neutral solution in the course of several days. When heated, the solid alkali metal salts decompose with the evolution of phosphorus(V) fluoride.

References

1. LANGE: *Ber.*, **61B**, 799 (1928).
2. LANGE and MÜLLER: *ibid.*, **63B**, 1058 (1930).
3. LANGE and V. KRUEGER: *ibid.*, **65B**, 1253 (1932).
4. LANGE: *Z. anorg. allgem. Chem.*, **208**, 387 (1932).

30. AMMONIUM METAVANADATE

$$V_2O_5 + Na_2CO_3 \rightarrow 2NaVO_3 + CO_2$$
$$NaVO_3 + NH_4Cl \rightarrow NH_4VO_3 + NaCl$$

SUBMITTED BY ROBERT H. BAKER,* HARRY ZIMMERMAN,† AND R. N. MAXSON*
CHECKED BY THERALD MOELLER‡ AND WARREN W. BRANDT‡

Ammonium metavanadate has been prepared by dissolving the oxide in either aqueous ammonia[1] or ammonium carbonate solution,[2] but the large quantities of water required with these reagents lower the ammonium-ion concentration to such an extent that crystallization is difficult. Vanadium(V) oxide reacts readily with a solution of sodium carbonate, and ammonium metavanadate may be precipitated from the resulting solution by the addition of an ammonium salt.

Procedure

Seventeen and one-half grams of anhydrous sodium carbonate is dissolved in 125 ml. of water in a 400-ml. beaker by warming and stirring. The solution is heated to boiling and 25 g. of commercial vanadium(V) oxide is added in small portions. When evolution of carbon dioxide has ceased, sufficient potassium permanganate (either solid or

* University of Kentucky, Lexington, Ky.
† Massachusetts Institute of Technology, Cambridge, Mass.
‡ University of Illinois, Urbana, Ill.

as a saturated solution) is added to discharge the blue color of the solution.*

The resulting suspension is filtered and the filtrate is poured repeatedly through the same filter until entirely clear. The residue is washed on the filter with water until a drop of the washings after being acidified with 6 N sulfuric acid gives no color with hydrogen peroxide. The combined filtrate and washings (about 125 to 150 ml.) are heated to about 60° and poured rapidly into a hot solution prepared by dissolving 75 g. of ammonium chloride in 125 ml. of water. Ammonium metavanadate is precipitated after a few hours. The crystals are removed by filtration, washed with 5-ml. portions of water until successive washings give no test for chloride ion, and air-dried. Yield 26 g. (80 per cent).

Properties

Ammonium metavanadate is a white crystalline material with a specific gravity of 2.326^{20}_{10}. Its solubility in water increases from 5.18 parts per 100 parts at 15° to 10.4 parts at 32°. When heated at relatively low temperatures, it loses both water vapor and ammonia and is converted to vanadium(V) oxide. At temperatures above 210°, further decomposition to lower vanadium oxides occurs.

References

1. DRAKE and SMITH: *J. Am. Chem. Soc.*, **52**, 4558 (1930).
2. SPENCER and JUSTICE: *ibid.*, **56**, 2306 (1934).

* Since an excess of permanganate is undesirable, it is recommended that a preliminary determination be made of the quantity needed for a small sample of the solution. The blue color of the solution arises from the fact that the commercial vanadium (V) oxide usually contains detectable quantities of lower valent oxides.

CHAPTER VI

31. SULFUR(VI) FLUORIDE

(Sulfur Hexafluoride)

$$S + 3F_2 \rightarrow SF_6$$

SUBMITTED BY WALTER C. SCHUMB*
CHECKED BY K. E. LONG† AND C. F. SWINEHART†

The combustion of sulfur in fluorine gas, which takes place when the two elements are brought together at room temperature, leads to the formation of a mixture of gases containing large proportions of the hexafluoride with small concentrations of lower fluorides, such as S_2F_2, SF_4, and S_2F_{10}.[3-5] If the fluorine is not purified to free it of contaminants generally found in the gas as delivered by an electrolytic generator, the presence of hydrogen fluoride, oxygen(II) fluoride, oxygen, or air may also be expected in the crude product.[4b] The purification of the sulfur(VI) fluoride consists in decomposing thermally the S_2F_{10} by passage through a nickel or Monel tube heated to about 400°, by which procedure the tetrafluoride and hexafluoride are formed; subjecting the gas mixture to a thorough washing and alkali scrubbing to remove hydrogen fluoride and the hydrolyzable lower fluorides of sulfur; and drying and condensing the hexafluoride to the solid state by adequate

* Massachusetts Institute of Technology, Cambridge, Mass.
† Harshaw Chemical Company, Cleveland, Ohio.

119

refrigeration, such as that provided by solid carbon dioxide. Storage of the liquid under about 350 p.s.i. gage pressure is conveniently provided by steel cylinders.[4b]

Procedure

For the laboratory preparation of sulfur(VI) fluoride, coarsely crushed lump (roll) sulfur is placed in a steel, copper, or Monel container, such as a horizontal pipe, capped at each end and provided with suitable inlet and outlet tubes, or a metal box provided with shelves placed in such a manner as to permit a current of fluorine to circulate over the sulfur charge in a continuous manner. If a pipe is used, sufficient space is allowed above the charge of sulfur for free passage of the gas.*

The apparatus depicted in Fig. 21 consists of a steel container A, roughly cubical in shape, about 15 in. on a side with a metal cover bolted securely on top, with an asbestos gasket to make the whole gastight. About 8 lb. of lump sulfur is placed on each of the several staggered shelves, in the container, and fluorine gas, provided by a generator operating on KF·2HF electrolyte at 100° (carbon anode), is passed in a circuitous path over the shelves in succession, entering at the top and leaving through an outlet at the bottom of the box. Since some of the lower fluorides are quite poisonous, it is important that all joints in the system be tight, to prevent leakage of gas into the air.†

The crude gas leaving the sulfur burner is purified by passing first through a Monel or nickel tube N (for example, a 7/8-in. tube 4 ft. long) with at least 12 in. of heated surface at the middle of the tube, brought to about 400° by external electric heating. This heating pyrolyzes the S_2F_{10}

---

* It is also practicable to maintain the charge of sulfur in the pipe above the melting point and to pass fluorine over the molten sulfur.

† It should be pointed out that the heat of reaction is considerable (262 kcal./mol), and that if the rate at which the fluorine is supplied to the sulfur is too rapid, there is danger that the container may be damaged. The data presented here refer to fluorine supplied by a relatively small cell (50 to 100 amp.).

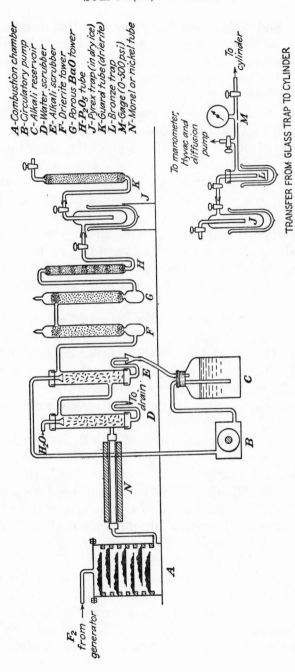

A—Combustion chamber
B—Circulatory pump
C—Alkali reservoir
D—Water scrubber
E—Alkali scrubber
F—Drierite tower
G—Porous BaO tower
H—P₂O₅ tube
J—Pyrex trap (in dry ice)
K—Guard tube (drierite)
L—Bronze trap
M—Gage (0–500 psi)
N—Monel or nickel tube

F_2 from generator

H_2O

To drain

To manometer, Hyvac and diffusion pump

To cylinder

TRANSFER FROM GLASS TRAP TO CYLINDER

Fig. 21.   Apparatus for the preparation of sulfur(VI) fluoride.

into SF_4 and SF_6. Subsequent purification consists of hydrolysis of the tetra- and monofluorides and absorption of other acidic components of the gas mixture, such as hydrogen fluoride or free fluorine, followed by drying. The gas issuing from the S_2F_{10} pyrolyzer passes first up through a vertical, packed copper tower D about 3 in. $\times$ 36 in. (filled with scrap copper), down through which water is being sprayed, leaving at the bottom of the tower through an S-shaped exit tube, which acts also as a liquid seal. From the top of the washing tower the gas passes next to the bottom of a second tower of steel E of approximately the same dimensions as the first, and packed with scrap iron or carbon. A spray of 1 N sodium hydroxide is circulated down through this alkali scrubber, by means of a small, motor-driven circulatory pump B, in conjunction with a supply carboy C of the solution, located below the tower.

The sulfur(VI) fluoride leaving the scrubbers, containing moisture and some air, next passes through three absorption towers F, G, and H filled with granular calcium sulfate, porous barium oxide, and phosphorus(V) oxide, respectively. These drying towers may be made of glass tubing or may consist of glass bottles filled with the absorbents and provided with inlet and outlet glass tubes.

For short-time storage, the sulfur(VI) fluoride is conveniently condensed in roomy pyrex traps that are cooled by an alcohol-solid carbon dioxide refrigerating bath J (or a similar combination). These traps may be, for example, about 20 to 25 cm. tall and 40 to 45 mm. wide with an inner (outlet) tube not less than 10 mm. wide leading down to within about 10 cm. from the bottom of the trap. Stopcocks are provided on inlet and outlet tubes.

For permanent storage the trap J containing the solid sulfur(VI) fluoride is connected through a ground joint to a metal system employed in transferring the contents to a steel cylinder. This metal system (conveniently made of copper or bronze) consists of a manifold tube leading from the cylinder through a metal trap L, which is about the same size as the pyrex trap, to the pyrex trap, which is also connected to a source of high vacuum, such as a mercury diffusion pump, backed by a Hyvac or similar oil pump. A manometer (not shown) teed into the line indicates the vacuum developed during evacuation of the transfer system. With the glass trap containing the solid hexafluoride immersed in liquid nitrogen, the entire system is pumped down to remove air or other inert gases. The metal trap is now cooled with the refrigerant and the glass trap allowed to warm up slowly, thus subliming the sulfur(VI) fluoride into the metal trap, which may then be shut off from the glass system by means of a valve. When the valve on the evacuated steel cylinder is opened and the metal trap allowed to warm up, the hexafluoride sublimes over into the cylinder. A pressure gage M teed into the manifold is helpful in indicating the progress of this procedure. The main valve of the cylinder is then closed and the contents of another glass trap are transferred in a similar fashion. When a sufficient quantity of the gas has thus been transferred to the cylinder and a gage pressure of about 350 p.s.i. has been attained, further addition of gas causes liquefaction of the cylinder contents and no further change in pressure is indicated on the gage. It is advisable not to fill the cylinder much over half full of liquid sulfur(VI) fluoride.

Properties

Sulfur(VI) fluoride is a colorless, odorless gas of high thermal stability and chemical inertness. It is unaffected by water or alkaline solutions or even by fused alkalies. It is decomposed by molten sodium and by electrical discharges, such as corona or spark discharge, particularly when in the presence of moisture or organic matter.

Its melting point is $-50.8° \pm 0.2°$;[2,5,6] at ordinary pressures it sublimes at $-63.7°$.[2,5,6] The vapor pressure may be expressed by the equations:

(a) for the solid:

$$\log_{10} P_{mm} = 8.765 - \frac{1231.3}{T};$$[6]

(b) for the liquid:

$$\log_{10} P_{mm.} = 7.705 - \frac{995.6}{T}$$

(over a small range of temperature)[5]

At 25° the pressure of liquid in a cylinder is about 330 p.s.i.;[4] the critical temperature is approximately 45°. It is perhaps the best gas for high-voltage insulation.[1a,b,4b] For other physical properties, see reference 4b.

References

1. a. BUECHNER, VAN DE GRAAFF, SPERDUTO, BURRILL, McINTOSH, and URQUHART: *Phys. Rev.*, **69**, 692 (1946).
   b. POLLOCK and COOPER, *ibid.*, **56**, 170 (1939).
2. KLEMM and HENKEL: *Z. anorg. allgem. Chem.*, **207**, 73 (1932).
3. MOISSAN and LEBEAU: *Compt. rend.*, **130**, 865 (1900); *Ann. chim. phys.*, [7], **26**, 147 (1902).
4. a. SCHUMB: *Phys. Rev.*, **69**, 692 (1946).
   b. SCHUMB: *Ind. Eng. Chem.*, **39**, 421 (1947).
5. SCHUMB and GAMBLE: *J. Am. Chem. Soc.*, **52**, 4302 (1930).
6. YOST and RUSSELL: "Systematic Inorganic Chemistry," p. 299, Prentice-Hall, Inc., New York, 1944.

32. DISULFUR PENTOXYDICHLORIDE

(Pyrosulfuryl Chloride)

$$2SO_3 + CCl_4 \rightarrow COCl_2 + S_2O_5Cl_2$$

SUBMITTED BY MICHAEL SVEDA*
MODIFIED AND CHECKED BY J. E. MALOWAN†

Disulfur pentoxydichloride is readily prepared by chlorinating sulfur trioxide with carbon tetrachloride. Since

* E. I. du Pont de Nemours and Company, Grasselli Chemicals Department, Experimental Laboratory, Cleveland, Ohio.

† Monsanto Chemical Company, Central Research Laboratories, Dayton, Ohio.

phosgene is obtained as a by-product, the entire reaction must be carried out in a well-ventilated hood. The recommended method is a modification of a procedure first reported by Sanger and Riegel.[1]

Disulfur pentoxydichloride has also been prepared by treating sulfur monochloride with sulfur trioxide vapor at low temperatures.[2]

Procedure

The reaction flask consists of a 2-l., three-necked, round-bottomed flask, equipped with an airtight stirrer and a reflux condenser to which a drying tube has been attached. The reactor is connected through the third opening with a second 2-l., three-necked flask by means of a 25-cm. length of wide glass tubing fitted with two male glass tapers. The second container, located vertically at a higher level than the reactor, serves as a distilling flask for generation of sulfur trioxide and is also equipped with a thermometer. The third neck of this flask is kept closed.

Eight hundred forty-six grams of carbon tetrachloride (5 mols + 10 per cent excess), previously dried over phosphorus(V) oxide, is placed in the reaction flask. Approximately 1700 g. of 65 per cent fuming sulfuric acid and a few boiling stones are placed in the distilling flask, which is then weighed. The reactor and generator are connected, and heat is applied to the latter, containing the fuming sulfuric acid, to effect slow distillation of sulfur trioxide into the reactor containing the carbon tetrachloride, which is stirred vigorously. The connecting tube acts as an air cooler. When the temperature of the residual sulfuric acid in the sulfur trioxide generator reaches 100°, the distillation is stopped. The flask is disconnected and weighed, the difference in weight indicating the amount of sulfur trioxide that has been distilled into the reaction vessel (about 800 g.).

During the addition of sulfur trioxide to the carbon tetrachloride no appreciable rise in temperature is observed and very little, if any, evolution of phosgene occurs. When the sulfur trioxide addition has been concluded (about 3 hours), the stirrer and connection tube are removed. A thermometer is inserted after addition of a few boiling stones. The other neck of the flask is closed.

Heat is applied gently to the reaction flask and refluxing is continued until the temperature of the reaction mixture reaches 140 to 142°. The reaction mixture is then distilled through a 40-cm. Vigreux column into a receiver protected by a drying tube. A little carbon tetrachloride comprises the first fraction. Next, a fraction varying in volume from 50 to 100 ml. is obtained at 137°. This is presumably a constant-boiling mixture of disulfur pentoxydichloride and chlorosulfonic acid, the latter resulting from the introduction of water with the sulfur trioxide. The desired product distills at 147 to 148°.* A 50 per cent yield would correspond to 538 g., based on the sulfur trioxide employed. The yield actually varies between 45 and 55 per cent.

Analysis

Disulfur pentoxydichloride may be analyzed by adding a weighed amount (0.5 to 1 g.) to 150 ml. of ice-cold water and allowing the mixture to stand until the disulfur pentoxydichloride, which at first forms an oily heavy drop, has disappeared by solution and hydrolysis in accordance with the equation:

$$S_2O_5Cl_2 + 3H_2O \rightarrow 2H_2SO_4 + 2HCl$$

An aliquot volume is then titrated with standard alkali and another portion is analyzed for chlorine by any one of the usual argentometric procedures. From the data, the purity

---

* Sanger and Riegel[1] recommend that the crude reaction product be washed with ice water, in order to remove chlorosulfonic acid, and then dried over phosphorus(V) oxide before the final distillation. The very slight increase in yield does not, however, justify the added effort.

Another method of purification consists in adding 20 g. of sodium chloride to the crude product and allowing the mixture to stand for 1 hour. It is then distilled under vacuum (b. 69 to 70°) at 43 mm. The chlorosulfonic acid contaminant presumably reacts with sodium chloride to give sodium chlorosulfonate that remains in the residue.

of the $S_2O_5Cl_2$ can be calculated. A typical analysis for a product prepared as outlined in the procedure follows: Calcd. for $S_2O_5Cl_2$: S, 29.82; Cl, 32.98. Found: S, 29.55; Cl, 32.88.

Properties

Disulfur pentoxydichloride fumes only slightly in air, possesses a pungent odor, and is insoluble in cold water. The product reacts rapidly with cold water if more than a few per cent of chlorosulfonic acid is present in the sample.

The lack of agreement in the literature concerning the physical constants of disulfur pentoxydichloride probably can be attributed to the presence of varying quantities of chlorosulfonic acid. The most reliable data are those reported by Sanger and Riegel, who describe it as a colorless liquid boiling at 152.5° at 766 mm., melting at −37°, with a density at 20° of 1.837 g./ml.

References

1. SANGER and RIEGEL: *Z. anorg. Chem.*, **76**, 79 (1912).
2. ROSE: *Pogg. Ann.*, **44**, 291 (1838).

33. SELENIUM(IV) OXIDE

(Selenium Dioxide)

$$Se + O_2 \rightarrow SeO_2$$

SUBMITTED BY S. Y. TYREE, JR.,* AND G. G. MARVIN†
CHECKED BY A. J. SOUKUP‡ AND L. F. AUDRIETH‡

Selenium(IV) oxide has been prepared by the oxidation of selenium using nitric acid,[2,3] vapors of fuming nitric acid,[2] oxygen, and oxygen admixed with nitrogen(IV) oxide.[1] When selenium is burned in oxygen a product is obtained that contains appreciable quantities of what is presumed to be red selenium as an impurity. While the combustion of

* University of North Carolina, Chapel Hill, N.C.,
† Materiels Branch, Production Division, U.S. Atomic Energy Commission, Washington D.C.
‡ University of Illinois, Urbana, Ill.

selenium in a mixture of oxygen and nitrogen(IV) oxide does give a product of high purity, it has been found that a snow-white product can be obtained more conveniently by burning selenium in oxygen and passing the vapors of the oxide through a layer of platinized asbestos that serves as a catalyst. A process embodying a similar principle makes use of solid oxide catalysts.[4]

Procedure

Apparatus. Oxidation is effected in the apparatus depicted in Fig. 22. The main combustion chamber is a 4-ft. length of 50-mm. pyrex tubing A, fitted at one end

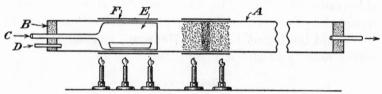

Fig. 22. Apparatus for combustion of selenium for the preparation of selenium(IV) oxide.

with a two-hole rubber stopper B, carrying an inlet tube for oxygen C and for air D. In order to prevent back diffusion of selenium(IV) oxide vapors, combustion is effected in a loading chamber E, constructed of 45-mm. tubing that is drawn down at one end and sealed to a 12-in. length of 10- to 12-mm. pyrex tubing extending through the two-hole rubber stopper. A 2-in. plug of pyrex glass wool is inserted just beyond the loading chamber, followed by a $\frac{1}{4}$- to $\frac{1}{2}$-in. layer of platinized asbestos held in place by a second 2-in. plug of glass wool.

The portion of the tube containing the catalyst is wrapped with $\frac{1}{32}$-in. sheet asbestos, which, in turn, is covered with a $\frac{1}{32}$-in. sheet copper sleeve. Sheet asbestos F is also wrapped around the portion of the combustion chamber where the boat containing selenium is located. The exit end of the combustion chamber is closed with a one-hole rubber stopper carrying a connecting tube that is vented to a suitable exhaust.

Platinized Asbestos. Approximately 2 g. of pure scrap platinum is dissolved in 40 ml. of hot aqua regia. The resulting solution is evaporated to dryness, the residue then treated with 20 ml. of 6 N hydrochloric acid, warmed, and the hot solution filtered into a 200-ml. casserole. Eight to ten grams of high-grade Gooch asbestos is added to the solution and stirred to allow complete absorption of the hexachloroplatinate(IV). The material is first dried and finally ignited in a muffle furnace at red heat. The resulting product, which possesses a uniform gray color, is shredded before use.

Selenium(IV) Oxide. Twenty-five grams of No. 4 selenium shot* is weighed into a pyrex or porcelain boat and placed in the loading chamber. The catalyst section is first heated with three wing-top burners to about 500° for 30 minutes while oxygen gas is passed slowly through the loading chamber. The portion of the tube containing the boat of selenium is next heated. The selenium melts at 220° and burns at a temperature of approximately 500° with a pale, greenish-blue flame. Combustion is regulated by controlling the oxygen flow. After burning has started, all four burners are used to keep the combustion zone at 500°. A slow stream of air, introduced at D, prevents back-diffusion of the selenium(IV) oxide vapors. The snow-white crystals of oxide sublime on the cooler portions of the tube beyond the catalyst zone. When the selenium has been consumed completely (less than 1 hour for the indicated quantity), all burners are turned off. The stream of air and of oxygen is kept flowing through the system while it is allowed to cool to room temperature. The product is then removed from the exit end of the tube. Yields in excess of 90 per cent are easily obtainable. In a typical run, 33.5 g. of selenium(IV) oxide, corresponding to 96

---

* Canadian Copper Refiners Limited, Montreal, Quebec.

per cent of theory, was obtained. The properties of selenium(IV) oxide have been described previously.[1,3]

References

1. NAESER: INORGANIC SYNTHESES, **1**, 117 (1939).
2. MEYER: *Ber.*, **55B**, 2082 (1922).
3. BAKER and MAXSON: INORGANIC SYNTHESES, **1**, 119 (1939).
4. CLARK and ELKIN: U.S. patent 2406666; *cf. Chem. Abstracts*, **40**, 7539 (1946).

34. SELENIUM(IV) OXYCHLORIDE

$$SeO_2 + 2HCl \rightarrow SeO_2 \cdot 2HCl$$
$$SeO_2 \cdot 2HCl + H_2SO_4 \rightarrow SeOCl_2 + H_2SO_4 \cdot H_2O$$

SUBMITTED BY G. B. L. SMITH[*†] AND JULIUS JACKSON[*]
CHECKED BY J. J. PITHA[‡] AND EVA BLANCHARD[‡]

Selenium(IV) oxychloride was synthesized first by Weber[10] in 1859 by heating together the vapors of selenium(IV) oxide and selenium(IV) chloride. It was later prepared by Michaelis[7] by the interaction of selenium(IV) oxide and phosphorus(V) chloride. Cameron and Macallam[2] allowed a mixture of selenium(IV) oxide and sodium chloride to interact and obtained sodium selenite and selenium(IV) oxychloride.

The classical researches of Victor Lenher on selenium(IV) oxychloride (reviewed by Smith[9]) were begun about 1919 at the University of Wisconsin. Lenher[5] suggested the following practical laboratory methods for the preparation of selenium(IV) oxychloride: (1) union of selenium(IV) oxide and selenium(IV) chloride; (2) partial hydrolysis of selenium(IV) chloride, and (3) dehydration of $SeO_2 \cdot 2HCl$ (dichloroselenious acid, $H_2SeO_2Cl_2$).[3,4,8]

The dehydration of $SeO_2 \cdot 2HCl$ was first effected by dis-

---

* Polytechnic Institute of Brooklyn, Brooklyn, N.Y.

† The assistance of Charles A. Lankau, Louis Lento, Jr., and Alvin Gordon, who at various times cooperated in the development of this synthesis, is hereby gratefully acknowledged.

‡ Kedzie Chemical Laboratories, Michigan State College, East Lansing, Mich.

tillation from "phosphorus(V) oxide, calcium chloride, or similar dehydrating agents."[5] The more convenient dehydration with sulfuric acid was developed subsequently by Muehlberger and Lenher.[8] The method outlined in detail here involves conversion of selenium to the oxide, reaction with hydrogen chloride to give dichloroselenious acid, and dehydration of the latter with sulfuric acid.

Procedure

Selenium(IV) Oxide. Selenium(IV) oxide is prepared by the oxidation of commercial selenium with commercial nitric acid following the method described by Baker and Maxson.[1] One kilogram of selenium is used and the selenium(IV) oxide is obtained by evaporation after the oxidation is completed. No further treatment of this product is necessary, since subsequent operations effect purification.

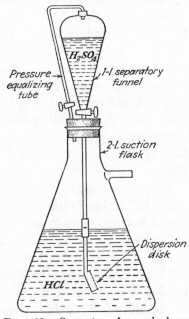

FIG. 23. Generator for anhydrous hydrogen chloride.

Pressure equalizing tube

H_2SO_4

1-l separatory funnel

2-l. suction flask

Dispersion disk

HCl

Anhydrous Hydrogen Chloride. Since considerable quantities of hydrogen chloride are needed in the conversion of selenium(IV) oxide to dichloroselenious acid, the apparatus described by Maxson[6] is modified as illustrated in Fig. 23.

Approximately 500 ml. of commercial hydrochloric acid (sp. gr., 1.18) is placed in the 3-l. suction flask that serves as the generating chamber. An equal volume of commercial sulfuric acid (sp. gr., 1.8) is placed in a 1-l. separatory funnel. The delivery tube of the funnel passes through a rubber stopper and extends to within $1\frac{1}{2}$ in. from the bottom of the flask. The lower end of this delivery tube is fitted with a sintered-glass gas dispersion tube or disk of large porosity and acts as a distributor so that the sulfuric acid may come in contact with the acid solution in a number of fine streams. A pressure-equalizing tube shown in the diagram completes the arrangement of the generator. The generation of hydrogen chloride is controlled by the rate at which the sulfuric acid is introduced into the generating chamber. The hydrogen chloride is dried by being passed through two towers containing sulfuric acid. When the hydrochloric acid is nearly "spent," bubbles of gas may be seen to form throughout the liquid and fresh hydrochloric acid should replace that in the generator. Caution. *Generation of hydrogen chloride is not without hazard. If sulfuric acid forms a separate layer under the hydrochloric acid, sudden mixing will cause the liberation of a very large volume of hydrogen chloride and even bursting of the flask may result. Quantities of acid will spatter about. It is believed that the arrangement used here minimizes this hazard, but the operation of the generator must be watched very carefully at all times.*

Preparation of Dichloroselenious Acid, $SeO_2 \cdot 2HCl$. Selenium(IV) oxide (1400 g. approx.) is placed in a tared 3-l. round-bottomed flask and two molecular equivalents (920 g.) of hydrogen chloride is passed into the flask, where it is absorbed by selenium(IV) oxide. It is advisable to place a 3-l. flask as a safety trap between the drying towers containing concentrated sulfuric acid and the reaction flask, as selenium(IV) oxide absorbs hydrogen chloride very rapidly to form liquid dichloroselenious acid. Hydrogen chloride is added until the gain in weight corresponds to that calculated. It is not necessary to weigh the reaction vessel and its contents until only approximately 100 g. of solid remains undissolved. When the calculated weight of hydrogen chloride has been absorbed, the remaining solid can be dissolved readily by agitation.

Dehydration of SeO₂·2HCl. For convenience in handling, the initial dehydration is carried out in small portions. Approximately 400 ml. of $SeO_2 \cdot 2HCl$ is placed in a 1-l. Erlenmeyer flask and 100 ml. of concentrated sulfuric acid (sp. gr. 1.84) is added. The materials are mixed thoroughly by swirling or agitation. Since appreciable quantities of hydrogen chloride are liberated at this point, the reaction is best carried out in a fume hood.* When the evolution of hydrogen chloride has ceased, the mixture is transferred to a 1-l. separatory funnel (pyrex is preferred because of the temperature of the solution) and is allowed to stand until it separates into layers. The partially dehydrated material constituting the lower layer may then be withdrawn. This operation is repeated with additional batches until all of the dichloroselenious acid has been subjected to initial dehydration.

A further dehydration of the product is necessary and may be accomplished as follows: a 450-ml. portion of selenium oxychloride is placed in a 600-ml. Erlenmeyer flask and 10 ml. of concentrated sulfuric acid is added. An emulsion forms and the whole mixture becomes opaque when the solution is agitated. The flask and contents are heated to about 50° and held at this temperature until two layers form. The hot solution is transferred to a separatory funnel and allowed to settle into layers again. The selenium oxychloride is withdrawn and is then treated with a 5-ml. portion of concentrated sulfuric acid. The resulting emulsion is again warmed until it separates into layers. The mixture is transferred to a separatory funnel and the layers are again separated. This procedure of treatment with 5-ml. portions of concentrated sulfuric acid, followed by heating to break the emulsion, is continued as long as an

* The liberation of hydrogen chloride must be due to a shift in the equilibrium existing in the liquid dichloroselenious acid. Evidently both hydrogen chloride and selenium(IV) oxide are soluble in $SeO_2 \cdot 2HCl$ without reaction. Addition of sulfuric acid for dehydration purposes raises the temperature of the system, thus decreasing the solubility of hydrogen chloride and causing it to be liberated.

emulsion of selenium oxychloride and sulfuric acid forms. When fully dehydrated, selenium oxychloride dissolves concentrated sulfuric acid completely.* These operations are repeated with other batches of selenium oxychloride until all the material has been completely dehydrated.

The dehydrated product is chlorinated at this point to convert any selenium(II) chloride that may be present into selenium(IV) chloride. The latter will react with sele-

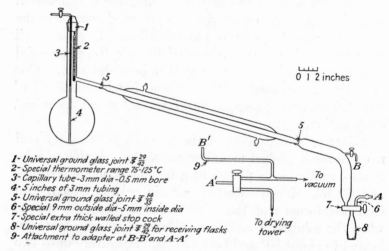

1- Universal ground glass joint $\frac{29}{42}$
2- Special thermometer range 75-125°C
3- Capillary tube -3mm dia -0.5 mm bore
4- 5 inches of 3mm tubing
5- Universal ground glass joint $\frac{14}{35}$
6- Special 9mm outside dia -5mm inside dia
7- Special extra thick walled stop cock
8- Universal ground glass joint $\frac{29}{42}$ for receiving flasks
9- Attachment to adapter at B-B' and A-A'

0 1 2 inches

To vacuum

To drying tower

FIG. 24. Apparatus for distillation and purification of selenium(IV) oxychloride.

nium(IV) oxide to form additional selenium(IV) oxychloride. The material before chlorination will be cherry-red in color; chlorine is bubbled carefully through the liquid until the color changes to straw-yellow.

The chlorinated material is distilled at 17 to 20 mm. pressure in the apparatus depicted in Fig. 24 and described in the purification step. Only a small amount of residue should be left if previous operations have been carried out properly. About 1750 to 1800 g. of selenium(IV) oxychlo-

---

* Too great an excess of sulfuric acid is as undesirable as incomplete dehydration, both resulting in lowered yields and difficult subsequent distillations.

ride should be obtained at this point, but a second distillation is necessary to ensure a good product.

Vacuum Distillation of Selenium Oxychloride. The crude selenium(IV) oxychloride is saturated with chlorine (if the color gives evidence of decomposition), and again distilled at 17 to 20 mm.,* using the apparatus shown in Fig. 24. The vacuum distilling apparatus consists of the following essential parts: capillary inlet, distilling flask, condenser, adapter, receiving flask, manifold, and three-way stopcocks. The distilling flask is of 750-ml. capacity, and the receiving flask, of 500-ml. capacity. The glass tubing, stopcocks, and ground-glass joints are of heavy construction because no lubricant other than sulfuric acid is used. Selenium(IV) oxychloride (500 ml.) is placed in the distilling flask, and the system is evacuated by means of a water pump to a pressure below 30 mm. The distilling flask is heated with a Glas-col mantle. The first 20 ml. of distillate is discarded; small samples are collected subsequently for determination of the melting point. When the product melts from 10.7 to 10.9° the distillation is continued until the solid selenium(IV) oxide accumulates in the distilling flask in sufficient quantity to cause violent bumping.† An average yield of about 1625 g. of purified selenium(IV) oxychloride will be obtained, corresponding to 80 per cent of theory based on a 1-kg. quantity of commercial selenium.

Transfer of Selenium(IV) Oxychloride. Since the pure substance is very hygroscopic, special precautions must be

* At pressures of 35 mm. the distillate contains sulfuric acid and products of the thermal decomposition of selenium oxychloride.

† If dichloroselenious acid is present in the selenium(IV) oxychloride, due to incomplete dehydration, extensive decomposition results during the distillation. Large volumes of hydrogen chloride will be evolved and substantial quantities of selenium dioxide will deposit in the distilling flask. The "bumping," as well as increase in pressure, occasionally causes ground-glass joints to become disconnected. Spattering of hot selenium oxychloride, which may result, introduces a serious hazard to the operator. The selenium oxychloride should always be tested for complete dehydration *immediately prior* to vacuum distillation using the method described under dehydration.

taken in storing and transferring it. It has been found advisable to store it in convenient-sized sealed glass ampoules. The siphon used in transferring selenium oxychloride is depicted in Fig. 25. The flask that has served as a receiver in the distilling apparatus is fitted with a ground-glass stopper carrying two tubes, A and B. One of these, A, is connected to a tower containing phosphorus(V) oxide. Air pressure may be applied to the latter to start the liquid selenium oxychloride through the siphon, B, for delivery into ampoules. The latter are sealed.

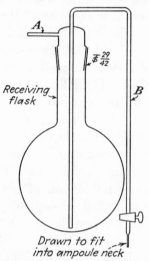

FIG. 25. Apparatus for the transfer of selenium(IV) oxychloride to ampoules.

Properties

Pure selenium(IV) oxychloride melts at 10.9 to 11° and boils at 177.2° (744 mm.).[11] It has a high dielectric constant (about 55 at 25°)[12] and is therefore an interesting nonprotonic solvent in which a wide variety of reactions may be caused to take place. The specific conductance of selenium(IV) oxychloride is also high (2.0×10^{-5} mho at 25°),[13] in which respect it is similar to sulfuric acid, and this property is probably related to the fact that these solvents are powerful solvolyzing agents.[9] It presumably undergoes autoionization in accordance with the equation:

$$2SeOCl_2 \rightleftharpoons (SeOCl \cdot SeOCl_2)^+ + Cl^-$$

and may therefore be regarded as the parent solvent of a system of compounds.[9] Pyridine and calcium chloride act as typical bases; arsenic(III) chloride, tin(IV) chloride, and sulfur trioxide, as acids. It forms solvates with many compounds, for example, $C_5H_5N \cdot SeOCl_2$ and $SnCl_4 \cdot 2SeOCl_2$.[9]

As an active inorganic acid chloride, the compound is

subject to rapid solvolysis when brought into contact with water, alcohols, ammonia, and amines. It is miscible with chlorinated hydrocarbons.

References

1. BAKER and MAXSON: INORGANIC SYNTHESES, **1**, 119 (1939).
2. CAMERON and MACALLAM: *Chem. News*, **59**, 267 (1889).
3. JACKSON and SMITH: *J. Am. Chem. Soc.*, **62**, 543 (1940).
4. LATIMER and HILDEBRAND: "Reference Book of Inorganic Chemistry," p. 205, The Macmillan Company, New York, 1933.
5. LENHER: *J. Am. Chem. Soc.*, **42**, 2498 (1920).
6. MAXSON: INORGANIC SYNTHESES, **1**, 147 (1939).
7. MICHAELIS: *Ann.*, **240**, 150 (1887).
8. MUEHLBERGER and LENHER: *J. Am. Chem. Soc.*, **47**, 1842 (1925).
9. SMITH: *Chem. Revs.*, **23**, 165 (1938).
10. WEBER: *Pogg. Ann.*, **108**, 615 (1859).
11. LENHER, SMITH, and TOWNE: *J. Phys. Chem.*, **26**, 156 (1922).
12. SMYTHE, LEWIS, GROSSMAN, and JENNINGS: *J. Am. Chem. Soc.*, **62**, 1219 (1940).
13. JULIEN: *ibid.*, **47**, 1799 (1925).

35. CRYSTALLINE SELENIC ACID

$$SeO_2 + H_2O_2 \rightarrow H_2SeO_4$$

SUBMITTED BY L. I. GILBERTSON* AND G. B. KING*
CHECKED BY S. Y. TYREE JR.†

Selenic acid has been prepared in a number of ways,[6] all of which are laborious, and only a few of which yield the concentrated acid in a state of high purity. Several authors[1-3,5,12,13,19] have prepared solutions of heavy-metal selenates and then precipitated the metal with hydrogen sulfide to give a dilute solution of the acid. The selenates were usually prepared by oxidation of the corresponding selenites with chlorine. Others[3,4,14,16,17] have oxidized suspensions of silver selenite with free halogen, then precipitated the silver halide to yield dilute solutions of selenic acid that could be concentrated by evaporation. Still othes[4,9,10] have electrolyzed solutions of selenates to effect removal of metallic ions, but this method has never been

* The State College of Washington, Pullman, Wash.
† The University of North Carolina, Chapel Hill, N.C.

considered to be a satisfactory one. Anodic oxidation of selenious acid solutions effects only incomplete oxidation and produces elementary selenium at the cathode.[4,8,11] Meyer and Heider[11] oxidized selenium(IV) oxide to selenic acid with hydrogen peroxide (30 per cent), but used other methods to prepare the concentrated acid.

Selenic acid is conveniently prepared by the oxidation of selenium(IV) oxide with 30 per cent hydrogen peroxide.[7] Water and selenious acid are the only possible impurities. The former can be removed effectively by evaporation under reduced pressure; the latter is present in small amount.

Procedure

One hundred fifty grams of resublimed selenium(IV) oxide[15] (synthesis 33) is dissolved in 100 ml. of distilled water in a round-bottomed flask of 1-l. capacity fitted with a standard taper joint. Five hundred grams of 30 per cent hydrogen peroxide (inhibitor-free)* is added slowly. An upright condenser is then attached (through an all-glass connection) to the flask and the mixture refluxed for 12 hours, during which time a stream of oxygen is passed through the solution to avoid bumping and to maintain an oxidizing atmosphere.

The refluxed selenic acid solution is transferred to a still so arranged as to permit a slow stream of dried air to pass through the solution.[18] Concentration of the solution by the removal of water is first carried out, using a water aspirator, and continued until the solution temperature has reached 150° (about 4 hours). A product containing 85 to 90 per cent selenic acid is obtained in this manner. Further dehydration may be accomplished by distillation at 1- to 2-mm. pressure and at temperatures not higher than 160°.† It is essential that overheating of the distilling

---

* Buffalo Electrochemical Company, Buffalo, N.Y.

† It is essential that this stage of the distillation be controlled very carefully, as temperatures in excess of 165° will cause decomposition of the selenic acid, according to the equation: $H_2SeO_4 \rightarrow H_2O + SeO_2 + \frac{1}{2}O_2$.

flask on the sides above the liquid level be avoided, as drops of selenic acid may be decomposed on this surface. A coil heater under the flask is therefore more desirable than immersion in an oil bath. Such distillation is continued until water no longer condenses in the receiver. If the selenic acid is not sufficiently dehydrated and even a few tenths of a per cent of water remains in the product, crystallization will be difficult.

After the final concentration, crystallization of selenic acid is effected by seeding. Solid selenic acid for seeding purposes may be obtained by cooling a portion of the acid with solid carbon dioxide. It is desirable that the seeding take place at a temperature somewhat below room temperature (10 to 15°). Crystallization of the solid is best carried out in a desiccator over some very efficient drying agent. The crystalline acid is dried by passing dry air [from phosphorus(V) oxide towers] over the crystals at a low pressure (5 mm.). The product contains 97 to 98 per cent selenic acid by analysis (the remainder being unoxidized selenious acid). Typical yields vary from 187 to 191 g., corresponding to 96 to 97.5 per cent of the theoretical based on selenium(IV) oxide as starting material.

Properties

Selenic acid is an extremely deliquescent crystalline solid melting at 55 to 58°. The specific gravity of 99 per cent selenic acid is 2.59 (20°).[3] At least two solid hydrates are known, $H_2SeO_4 \cdot H_2O$ and $H_2SeO_4 \cdot 4H_2O$. The acid is similar to sulfuric acid with respect to ionization in water. It is, however, more easily reduced than sulfuric acid, moderately strong solutions of hydrochloric acid being sufficient to reduce selenic to selenious acid. Selenates are usually isomorphous with the corresponding sulfates.

References

1. Benger: *J. Am. Chem. Soc.*, **39**, 2171 (1917).
2. Cameron and Macallam: *Chem. News*, **59**, 219, 232, 258, 267 (1889).

3. DIEMER and LENHER: *J. Phys. Chem.*, **13**, 505 (1909).
4. DENNIS and KOLLER: *J. Am. Chem. Soc.*, **41**, 949 (1919).
5. VON GERICHTEN: *Ber.*, **6**, 162 (1873).
6. GILBERTSON: *Northwest Sci.*, **5**, 83 (1931).
7. GILBERTSON and KING: *J. Am. Chem. Soc.*, **58**, 180 (1936).
8. GLAUSER: *Chem. Ztg.*, **31**, 630 (1907).
9. MATHERS: *J. Am. Chem. Soc.*, **30**, 1374 (1908).
10. METZNER: *Compt. rend.*, **127**, 54 (1898).
11. MEYER and HEIDER: *Ber.*, **48**, 1154 (1915).
12. MEYER and MOLDENHAUER: *Z. anorg. allgem. Chem.*, **116**, 193 (1921).
13. MITSCHERLICH: *Pogg. Ann.*, **9**, 623 (1827).
14. MORRIS: *Trans. Wisconsin Acad. Sci.*, **19**(I), 369 (1918).
15. NAESER: INORGANIC SYNTHESES, **1**, 117 (1939);
16. STONE: *J. Am. Chem. Soc.*, **45**, 29 (1923).
17. THOMSEN: *Ber.*, **2**, 598 (1869).
18. WEBER and KING: INORGANIC SYNTHESES, **1**, 101 (1939).
19. WOHLWILL: *Ann.*, **114**, 169 (1860).

36. TELLURIUM(IV) CHLORIDE

(Tellurium Tetrachloride)

$$\text{Te} + 2\text{Cl}_2 \rightarrow \text{TeCl}_4$$

SUBMITTED BY JOHN F. SUTTLE* AND CHARLES R. F. SMITH*
CHECKED BY A. D. McELROY,† W. E. BENNETT,† AND J. KLEINBERG†

Tellurium(IV) chloride is most conveniently prepared by the direct union of the elements,[1] but is also obtainable by the reaction of elemental tellurium or tellurium(IV) oxide with various anhydrous chlorides such as sulfur chloride, iron(III) chloride, and selenium(IV) chloride.[2-4] Tellurium of 99.95 per cent purity and chlorine of similar purity are easily obtainable. The absence of other reaction products in the direct union simplifies the purification problem.

Procedure

The all-glass apparatus depicted in Fig. 26 is constructed of such size that it will fit completely into a small oven to

* University of Portland, Portland, Ore.
† University of Kansas, Lawrence, Kans.

facilitate drying. The apparatus is dried for 12 hours at 100°. The size of the flask and the number of ampoules can, however, be varied depending upon the total amount and size of the samples of tellurium(IV) chloride desired.

Fifty grams (0.392 mol) of tellurium is placed in the flask immediately upon removal from the oven. The flask is stoppered and a slow stream of chlorine is introduced through the 8-mm. side tube shown in the figure. A

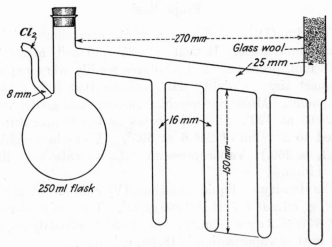

FIG. 26. Apparatus for the preparation of tellurium(IV) chloride.

Bunsen burner flame may be necessary to initiate the reaction. When the reaction has started, heat is no longer necessary in the early stages. The presence of tellurium(II) chloride is indicated by the murky black liquid that first forms, and by the brown vapor [resembling nitrogen(IV) oxide] present above the liquid when heat is applied. As soon as an excess of chlorine has been added to complete the conversion of the tellurium to the tetrachloride, the liquid changes to a dark red color and becomes clear. A yellow vapor is produced by heating the red liquid. This condenses on the cool part of the apparatus and solidifies into a yellowish-white crystalline material. The tellurium(IV) chloride is distilled into the ampoules and the ampoules sealed off. The slow stream of chlorine is continued throughout the distillation and sealing operations. Conversion is quantitative. With care in distillation, yields above 95 g. (90 per cent) are readily obtainable.* *Anal.* Calcd. for $TeCl_4$: Te, 47.36; Cl, 52.64. Found: Te, 47.9, 47.76; Cl, 53.34; 53.70.

Properties[1]

Tellurium(IV) chloride is a white crystalline solid at room temperature. It melts at 225° and boils at 390° at 755.6 mm. pressure. It hydrolyzes readily when exposed to moist air. Solubility data indicate that it is a polar compound. Molecular-weight measurements give a value of 290.3 at 420°, which decreases as the temperature is raised to a value of 246.6 at 595°. (Formula weight of $TeCl_4$ is 269.) Vapor pressure data indicate very little association.

The density of liquid tellurium(IV) chloride at 232° is 2.559 g./ml.; at 427° it is 2.260 g./ml. The surface tension at 238° is 40.2 dynes/cm.; and at 413.5° it is 26.9 dynes/cm. The heat of vaporization is 18,400 cal./mol.

References

1. SIMONS: *J. Am. Chem. Soc.,* **52**, 3488 (1930).
2. LENHER and HILL: *ibid.,* **30**, 737 (1908).
3. LENHER: *ibid.,* **30**, 741 (1908).
4. LENHER: *ibid.,* **43**, 29 (1921).

* The precautions to be observed in preparation of tellurium(IV) chloride may be summarized as follows: (1) completely anhydrous conditions; (2) a side arm 20 to 25 mm. in diameter on the flask to prevent plugging by deposition of solid tellurium(IV) chloride; (3) a slow stream of chlorine to prevent excessive entrainment of tellurium(IV) chloride, which may blow the glass wool plug out of the outlet and lower the yield; (4) location of the side arm about an inch above the bulb of the flask so that heating will not be excessive. Constrictions in the ampoules at the sealing-off place are not necessary since the operation is carried out at atmospheric pressure and the tellurium(IV) chloride does not affect the properties of the glass.

37. TELLURIUM(IV) OXIDE

(Tellurium Dioxide)

$$Te + 2[O] \rightarrow TeO_2$$

Submitted by H. Marshall*
Checked by A. J. King† and Thomas Harr†

Tellurium(IV) oxide has been prepared by the combustion of elementary tellurium, and by the ignition of telluric acid. The usual methods, first employed by Berzelius, involve either ignition of so-called "basic tellurium nitrate," $2TeO_2 \cdot HNO_3$, or hydrolytic precipitation from hot nitric or hydrochloric acid solutions.[1] When adequately pure tellurium is the raw material, the hydrolysis of a concencentrated hydrochloric acid solution is a simple and efficient method; unfortunately, some commercial grades of tellurium contain antimony and bismuth as major impurities. The method given below is designed to give both high purity and high yield irrespective of the initial purity. A unique feature is the solution of the tellurium fairly free of associated impurities at the outset. Succeeding steps involve the fractional precipitation of bismuth and antimony,[2] the crystallization of basic tellurium nitrates, and finally decomposition at temperatures above 300°[3] to yield tellurium(IV) oxide. Lead, when present in small amounts, and other possible heavy-metal contaminants are soluble in nitric acid of high concentration.

Procedure

Twenty grams of commercial tellurium (finer than 60 mesh) is weighed into a 1000-ml. beaker, covered with 200 ml. of water, and treated by the slow addition of 95 ml. of concentrated nitric acid (sp. gr. 1.42). The reaction is

---

* Canadian Copper Refiners Limited, Montreal East, Quebec.
† Syracuse University, Syracuse, N.Y.

allowed to continue for 5 to 10 minutes* with occasional agitation. Insoluble impurities are removed immediately by filtration on a Büchner funnel. The filtrate is transferred to a 600-ml. beaker.

Sixty-five milliliters of concentrated nitric acid is then added and the solution boiled until oxides of nitrogen have been expelled. Basic nitrates of antimony and bismuth precipitate at this point if these substances are present as impurities. These are removed by filtering through asbestos, after which the clear liquor is evaporated gently on a water bath under a hood in an open 600-ml. beaker. Basic tellurium nitrate is deposited. The evaporation is continued until the solution volume has been reduced to 100 ml. The solution is then cooled. The crystalline deposit is filtered, washed with water on a suction filter, and air-dried.

The crystals are placed in a 400-ml. beaker, covered by inverting a 1000-ml. beaker over the other, and heated at a hot-plate temperature of 400 to 430° for 2 hours. The tellurium(IV) oxide is cooled and bottled immediately to avoid slow darkening due to reduction by organic matter from the atmosphere. In a typical experiment, 21 g. of TeO_2 (84 per cent of theory) was obtained from a tellurium sample containing: Cu, 0.05 per cent; Fe, 0.015 per cent; Pb, 0.005 per cent; Se, 0.05 per cent; alloyed with 0.3 per cent each As, Sb, and Bi. The product was found to contain: Te, 79.91 per cent (theory 79.95 per cent); Cu, 0.00002 per cent; Fe, 0.0007 per cent; Pb, 0.0018 per cent; Se, As, Sb, and Bi, less than 0.001 per cent.

Properties

Tellurium(IV) oxide is a white solid existing in two crystalline forms, the tetragonal (sp. gr. 3.66), obtained by hydrolysis or ignition of the nitrate below 350°, and the

---

* Many samples of tellurium contain selenide and telluride impurities which are attacked if the reaction time is extended. By limiting the reaction time some purification can be effected in the initial step. (H. M.)

rhombic (sp. gr. 3.93), obtained at higher temperatures. On heating, tellurium(IV) oxide becomes yellowish and finally melts at a dull red heat to a deep yellow liquid. The exact melting point is not known.

It is perceptibly soluble in water to give a neutral solution. It is soluble both in sodium hydroxide solutions and in hydrochloric acid. It is converted into a basic tellurium sulfate by heating to the appearance of white fumes with sulfuric acid.

References

1. BERZELIUS: *Pogg. Ann.*, **32**, 15 (1834); *Ann. chim. phys.*, [2] **58**, 129 (1835).
2. KÖTHNER: *Ann.*, **319**, 1 (1901).
3. NORRIS: *J. Am. Chem. Soc.*, **28**, 1675 (1906).

38. TELLURIC ACID

$$5TeO_2 + 2KMnO_4 + 6HNO_3 + 12H_2O$$
$$\rightarrow 5H_6TeO_6 + 2KNO_3 + 2Mn(NO_3)_2$$

SUBMITTED BY FRANK C. MATHERS,* CHARLES M. RICE,* HOWARD BRODERICK,* AND ROBERT FORNEY*
CHECKED BY A. J. KING† AND T. HARR†

Although similar to sulfur dioxide in many ways, tellurium(IV) oxide cannot be oxidized to the hexavalent state by nitric acid. While many of the stronger oxidizing agents will accomplish this oxidation, potassium permanganate in a nitric acid solution is preferred[1] since the by-products of this reaction are sufficiently soluble in water and in nitric acid solution to make possible a satisfactory separation from the telluric acid which is only slightly soluble in water and very insoluble[2] in concentrated nitric acid.

Procedure

Five grams of potassium permanganate is dissolved in 100 ml. of water and the resulting solution added slowly

* Indiana University, Bloomington, Ind.
† Syracuse University, Syracuse, N.Y.

with vigorous stirring, in 5-ml. portions at 5-minute intervals, to a boiling suspension of 10 g. of tellurium(IV) oxide* (synthesis 37) in 40 ml. of concentrated nitric acid and 100 ml. of water. Some manganese(IV) oxide is produced with each addition of permanganate. It is possible, but not necessary, to effect its solution, except near the end, by boiling for a sufficient time after each portion of permanganate has been added.† After all the permanganate has been added the solution is kept at the boiling point for 50 minutes in order to reduce the amount of manganese(IV) oxide. Three per cent hydrogen peroxide is then slowly added until the remaining manganese(IV) oxide goes into solution. About 50 ml. will be required.

The clear solution is evaporated until its weight has been decreased to about 60 g. Ten milliliters of concentrated nitric acid is added and the solution allowed to stand for 24 hours. The mother liquor is decanted from the crystals, evaporated to a weight of 25 g., and again treated with 10 ml. of concentrated nitric acid. A second crop of crystals is obtained after an additional 24 hours.

The combined crops of crystals are washed with three portions of 10 ml. each of concentrated nitric acid and drained as completely as possible after each washing. A centrifuge is desirable in conducting this washing operation. The product is then purified by crystallizing from a hot mixture of 25 ml. of water and 17 ml. of concentrated nitric acid.‡ These crystals should be washed with nitric acid,

* Crude tellurium dioxide can be used with equally good results, if the sand and other insoluble materials are removed by filtration following the addition of the hydrogen peroxide.

† The amount of manganese(IV) oxide remaining in the reaction mixture at the end depends upon (1) the excess of permanganate used, (2) the rate of addition of the permanganate, and (3) the time of boiling between additions of the permanganate. As the insoluble tellurium(IV) oxide is oxidized to soluble telluric acid, the solution gradually becomes free of any precipitate except for the manganese(IV) oxide.

‡ If a high yield is not important, it is recommended that the product be recrystallized from water after one recrystallization from the nitric acid.

preferably by centrifugation. High-purity telluric acid is obtained after a third recrystallization, followed by removal of adhering water and nitric acid from the centrifuged crystals by heating to 100° for 1 hour, then crushing and grinding and reheating for 15 minutes to remove occluded mother liquor. The final crystals have a purity of 99.85 per cent. The over-all material yield will vary from 11 to 12.5 g., or 76.5 to 86.8 per cent. If large, well-formed crystals are desired, it is necessary to effect their formation from water solution; the solubility of the telluric acid in nitric acid is so small that large crystals cannot be produced easily. Crystals from water solutions are more easily freed from solvent than those obtained from nitric acid.

Analysis

Telluric acid can be titrated as a monobasic acid[3] with standard sodium hydroxide using phenolphthalein as an indicator, if an equal volume of glycerol is added. If any nitric acid is present, it must be neutralized first with sodium hydroxide, using methyl orange as indicator.

Properties

Telluric acid, $H_2TeO_4 \cdot 2H_2O$, has a solubility[2] at 25° of 0.97 g. per 100 ml. in nitric acid containing 57.39 g. HNO_3 per 100 ml. of solution, and 35.8 g. in a nitric acid containing 8.63 g. of HNO_3 per 100 ml. The first ionization constant has a value of $K_A = 6 \times 10^{-7}$. It is a weak acid and a weak oxidizing agent. Only the alkali metal and ammonium salts are soluble in water. It is stable below about 140°.

References

1. MATHERS, RICE, BRODERICK, and FORNEY: Proc. Ind. Acad. Sci., 52, 114 (1943).
2. MATHERS and RICE: ibid., 52, 117 (1943).
3. ROSENHEIM and WEINHEBER: Z. anorg. Chem., 69, 266 (1910); cf. Chem. Abstracts, 5, 1378 (1911).

39. CHROMIUM(II) ACETATE

(Chromous Acetate)

$$CrCl_3 \cdot aq. + e^- \rightarrow CrCl_2 \cdot aq. + Cl^-$$
$$CrCl_2 \cdot aq. + 2NaC_2H_3O_2 \rightarrow Cr(C_2H_3O_2)_2 + 2NaCl + aq.$$

SUBMITTED BY M. R. HATFIELD[*]
CHECKED BY HELEN MATHESON[†] AND JACOB KLEINBERG[†]

The procedure and apparatus described by Balthis and Bailar[1] have been modified to eliminate certain handling difficulties and to give increased yields of chromium(II) acetate. Reduction of the chromium(III) ion is effected by using a Jones reductor. This makes it unnecessary to filter the chromium(II) chloride solution. The reductor may be used for a number of preparations without replenishing the zinc. The chromium(II) chloride solution is run from the reductor directly into the sodium acetate solution to ensure complete use of all the chromium(II) salt. Transfer of the reaction slurry from the bottom of the reaction flask to a filter makes it possible to dry completely and process the precipitate under nonoxidizing conditions.

Procedure

The apparatus is set up as indicated in Fig. 27. The reductor[2] column A has a 2-cm. i.d. and is fitted at B with a 2-cm. plug of glass wool. The zinc amalgam column is about 45 cm. in height. The special stopcock C has a 10-mm. i.d.; the connection to the reaction flask D is made with rubber tubing. Funnel E is a coarse, sintered-glass filter, about 4 in. in diameter. The glass stirring rod F is so located that good mixing of the precipitate with the washing agents, and mixing during the drying process, are possible.

Nitrogen‡ is passed through the reaction flask during the entire precipitation and is passed over the precipitate

---

* University of Illinois, Urbana, Ill.
† University of Kansas, Lawrence, Kans.
‡ The checkers found natural gas to be more satisfactory.

during filtration. The nitrogen is freed from oxygen by passing it through towers filled with alkaline pyrogallol and ammoniacal copper(I) chloride.

The zinc is amalgamated for use in the Jones reductor by stirring a quantity of 10- to 20-mesh zinc for 10 minutes in

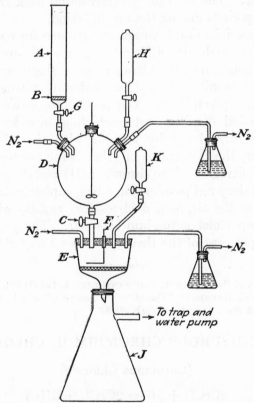

FIG. 27. Arrangement of apparatus for the preparation of chromium(II) acetate.

a solution containing 0.1 M mercury(II) chloride in 1 M hydrochloric acid. The zinc column is washed thoroughly with water and then with a small quantity of 1 N sulfuric acid. The liquid level in the reductor is at all times kept above the top of the zinc column.

Ninety grams of chromium(III) chloride 6-hydrate is dissolved in 120 ml. of water and 30 ml. of 2 N sulfuric acid. The solution is poured into the reductor column and the rate of flow through the column adjusted by stopcock *G* so that the chromium salt solution dropping into the reaction flask *D* is bright blue in color. As soon as this condition is achieved, a filtered solution of 252 g. of sodium acetate in 325 ml. of water is added to the reaction flask through *H*. The mixture in the reaction flask *D* is stirred for short periods during the precipitation.

When precipitation is complete, nitrogen (or natural gas) is passed through funnel *E* and stopcock *C* is opened. By careful regulation of the nitrogen rate a slight suction may be applied to filter flask *J* so that only nitrogen passes through the precipitate. The precipitate is washed with freshly boiled distilled water which is introduced at *K*. Drying is carried out by washing with alcohol and then with ether, the last traces of ether being removed by the stream of nitrogen. The chromium(II) acetate precipitate, which is a deep red powder, must be completely dry* before exposure to the air, as it oxidizes very rapidly when moist to the deep violet chromium(III) salt. The yield is 55.0 g., or 95 per cent of the theoretical based on $CrCl_3 \cdot 6H_2O$.

References

1. BALTHIS and BAILAR: INORGANIC SYNTHESES, **1**, 123 (1939).
2. PIERCE and HAENISCH: "Quantitative Analysis," 3d ed., p. 225, John Wiley & Sons, Inc., New York, 1948.

40. ANHYDROUS CHROMIUM(II) CHLORIDE

(Chromous Chloride)

$$2CrCl_3 + H_2 \rightarrow 2CrCl_2 + 2HCl$$

SUBMITTED BY ANTON B. BURG†
CHECKED BY RALPH C. YOUNG‡ AND CHAUNCY STARR‡

Anhydrous chromium(II) chloride has been prepared by three essentially different methods: (1) by treatment of

---

* A 24-hour drying period was found to be necessary in order to produce a stable product. (H. M. and J. K.)

† University of Southern California, Los Angeles, Calif.
‡ Massachusetts Institute of Technology, Cambridge, Mass.

anhydrous chromium(III) chloride with hydrogen at red heat;[1,2] (2) by the action of hydrogen chloride upon metallic chromium[3,4]; and (3) by the dehydration of hydrated chromium(II) chloride *in vacuo* at 180°.[5] The last method does not give a pure product; oxidation, hydrolysis, or both occur. The product of the second method is often contaminated with metal.[6] The first method is best; partial reduction to metal may occur but can be prevented by using a mixture of hydrogen and hydrogen chloride.[7]

Procedure A

A Vycor or silica tube, 60 cm. long with a 15-mm. bore, is baked for 1 hour at 450° while a current of dry hydrogen chloride is passed through it. The tube is cooled and the hydrogen chloride is replaced by dry air. Five grams of anhydrous chromium(III) chloride[8] is introduced into the tube and purified by sublimation in a current of dry chlorine or dry hydrogen chloride at 800°. The gas stream is adjusted to pass at a rate of 20 to 30 ml. per minute, this rate of flow providing for the formation of large flakes. Iron(III) chloride that may appear is sublimed and caused to collect at the end of the tube. After it is removed, the purified chromium(III) chloride that is deposited at the end of the furnace can be obtained.

The apparatus employed for the reduction is shown in Fig. 28. A pyrex reaction tube 2.5 × 50 cm., previously heated *in vacuo* at 500°, is fitted with a two-hole rubber stopper carrying an outlet tube *A* and the longer tube *B*, 8 mm. in diameter, for leading the gases to the closed end; this tube should slip rather easily into the rubber stopper. The sublimed chromium(III) chloride is spread out toward the closed end of the reaction tube and the latter is placed in an electric resistance furnace, the temperature of which can be measured with a thermocouple. Dry oxygen-free hydrogen and hydrogen chloride,[9] each at the rate of 50 ml. per minute, are passed first into a T-tube where they mix, and then led to the closed end of the reaction vessel.* To the exit tube A is attached a drying tube containing anhydrous calcium chloride. The reduction is carried out at 500°. The furnace may be slipped off at intervals to inspect the product, which is white when pure.

After the reaction is complete, the furnace is cooled to room temperature and a current of dry carbon dioxide or dry nitrogen is substituted for the hydrogen–hydrogen chloride mixture. The delivery tube is pulled through the rubber stopper until the end passes the constriction C at which the apparatus is then sealed.

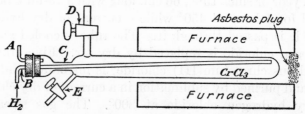

FIG. 28.   Apparatus for effecting reduction of chromium(III) chloride.

The larger stopcock D has a 10-mm. bore. Through it the product can be transferred as needed, provided this operation is carried out in an atmosphere of a dry inert gas such as nitrogen or carbon dioxide which can be introduced through the small stopcock E.

Procedure B

This synthesis can also be accomplished by using a column of chromium(II) chloride as a "getter" for a second column of the salt. A Vycor tube, 90-cm. by 13-mm. bore, baked out as described in procedure A, is used for this purpose. Sublimed chromium(III) chloride is introduced in such a way that two columns are formed, each being 10 cm. long and separated from each other by a distance of 20 cm. The materials are held in place by glass wool. Two Hoskins furnaces (hinged type) are used in line, a

---

* The procedure described by McCoy, INORGANIC SYNTHESES, **2**, 72, (1946) may also be used for producing a 1:1 mixture of hydrogen and hydrogen chloride.

column of salt being located at the center of each furnace. The salt is sublimed at 800° in a current of hydrogen chloride and cooled in a current of the gas. The position of each furnace is then changed so that again the chloride is at the center. The reduction is carried out with a mixture of hydrogen and hydrogen chloride at 500°, as described in procedure A. When reduction is complete, the furnaces are cooled to room temperature and dry carbon dioxide is substituted for the hydrogen–hydrogen chloride mixture. The product can then be transferred in a current of carbon dioxide into a suitable container.

Properties

Pure anhydrous chromium(II) chloride forms white hygroscopic needles that are stable in dry air but oxidize rapidly if moist. The compound dissolves in water, forming the blue hydrated chromium(II) ion which has strong reducing properties. Several hydrates[5,10] and ammines[7] have been described.

References

1. MOBERG: *J. prakt. Chem.*, **29**, 175 (1843); **44**, 322 (1848).
2. PELIGOT: *Ann. chim. phys.*, [3] **12**, 528 (1844).
3. UFER: *Ann.*, **112**, 302 (1859).
4. MOISSAN: *Compt. rend.*, **92**, 792 (1881).
5. KNIGHT and RICH: *J. Chem. Soc.*, **99**, 89 (1911).
6. KOPPEL: *Z. anorg. Chem.*, **45**, 359 (1905).
7. SCHLESINGER and HAMMOND: *J. Am. Chem. Soc.*, **55**, 3971 (1933).
8. HEISIG, FAWKES, and HEDIN: INORGANIC SYNTHESES, **2**, 193 (1946).
9. MAXSON: *ibid.*, **1**, 147 (1939).
10. BALTHIS and BAILAR: *ibid.*, 125 (1939).

41. HEXAMMINECHROMIUM(III) NITRATE

$$CrCl_3 + 6NH_3 \xrightarrow[-33°]{NaNH_2} [Cr(NH_3)_6]Cl_3$$

$$[Cr(NH_3)_6]Cl_3 + 3HNO_3 \rightarrow [Cr(NH_3)_6](NO_3)_3 + 3HCl$$

SUBMITTED BY A. L. OPPEGARD* AND J. C. BAILAR, JR.*
CHECKED BY JACOB KLEINBERG†

By the action of liquid ammonia on anhydrous chromium(III) chloride, Christensen[1] prepared a mixture of

* University of Illinois, Urbana, Ill.
† University of Kansas, Lawrence, Kans.

chloropentamminechromium(III) chloride and hexamminechromium(III) chloride. Separation was effected by extraction of the soluble hexammine, which was then precipitated as the nitrate by the addition of concentrated nitric acid. Rollinson and Bailar[2] prepared hexamminechromium(III) nitrate in low yield by treating anhydrous chromium(III) sulfate with liquid ammonia in the presence of ammonium nitrate. They also prepared the hexammine by dissolving chloropentamminechromium(III) nitrate in liquid ammonia containing a little sodium amide. The following procedure utilizes the observation of Rollinson and Bailar that sodium amide (a base in liquid ammonia) catalyzes the ammonation of the chloropentamminechromium(III) ion.

Procedure

(Caution. *Use a well-ventilated hood.*)

About 800 ml. of liquid ammonia is introduced into a 1-l. Dewar flask, or a 1000-ml. beaker that is placed within a 1500-ml. beaker, and 0.5 g. of clean sodium metal and 0.2 g. of iron(II) ammonium sulfate are added.[3] After the blue color of the sodium has disappeared, 50 g. (approximately 0.3 mol) of anhydrous chromium(III) chloride[4] is added in 2-g. portions, while the solution is constantly stirred. After the addition has been completed (1 to 2 hours), the brown precipitate is allowed to settle, and the clear, slightly colored supernatant liquid is decanted from the beaker or siphoned from the Dewar flask.

The residue is transferred to a large crystallizing or evaporating dish and is allowed to stand with occasional stirring until the odor of ammonia is gone and a bright yellow, freely flowing powder remains.* The yield of impure [Cr(NH$_3$)$_6$]Cl$_3$ is about 80 g. (nearly quantitative). For purification, the material is quickly dissolved in a mixture of 150 ml. of water and 10 ml. of concentrated hydrochloric acid at 40°, and filtered. The filtrate is

---

* Hexamminechromium(III) salts are slightly photosensitive and should be protected from direct sunlight.

immediately treated with 50 ml. of concentrated nitric acid and is cooled to room temperature. Pure hexamminechromium(III) nitrate precipitates. After standing for a few minutes, the bright yellow, crystalline salt is collected on a Büchner funnel and is washed with cold distilled water containing a little nitric acid, then with alcohol, and finally with ether. The product is dried in a vacuum desiccator protected from strong light, and is stored in a brown bottle. The yield of hexamminechromium(III) nitrate is 80 g. (75 per cent).

Properties

The other salts of the series, except the normal sulfate, can be prepared by metathesis. In the dry state the salts are stable unless exposed to light or heated above 100°, at which temperature slow decomposition begins. The chloride, sulfate, and nitrate are moderately soluble in water at room temperature, the solubility of the nitrate being 1 part in 40 parts of water. The nitrate is only sparingly soluble in the presence of nitric acid. Since neutral solutions decompose slowly upon standing at room temperature and rapidly at elevated temperatures, care should be taken to perform crystallizations rapidly and at moderate temperatures.

When heated in the presence of hydrochloric acid, the hexammine salts are converted to chloropentamminechromium(III) chloride, $[Cr(NH_3)_5Cl]Cl_2$. A pronounced tendency to form double salts exists. For example, the chloride forms a double salt with mercury(II) chloride; and the nitrate in the presence of the sulfate ion reacts to form the sparingly soluble compound $[Cr(NH_3)_6](SO_4)(NO_3)$. For this reason, the normal sulfate must be made from the hydroxide of the series.

References

1. CHRISTENSEN: *Z. anorg. Chem..* **4,** 229 (1893).
2. ROLLINSON and BAILAR: *J. Am. Chem. Soc.,* **65,** 250 (1943).
3. GREENLEE and HENNE: INORGANIC SYNTHESES, **2,** 128 (1946).
4. HEISIG, FAWKES, and HEDIN: *ibid.,* 193 (1946).

42. CHROMIUM HEXACARBONYL

$$CrCl_3 + C_6H_5MgBr \xrightarrow{CO} [complex] \xrightarrow{H_2O} Cr(CO)_6$$

SUBMITTED BY B. B. OWEN,* J. ENGLISH, JR.,* H. G. CASSIDY,* AND C. V. DUNDON*
CHECKED BY G. CALINGAERT† AND V. F. HUIZDA†

Chromium hexacarbonyl has been prepared by the reaction of chromium(III) chloride with phenylmagnesium bromide in the presence of carbon monoxide.[1-3] Unsatisfactory yields have been reported and difficulty experienced in repeating the synthesis.[4,5] Unfortunately, no other methods for the preparation of this substance are recorded in the literature.

Procedure A

Preparation under Carbon Monoxide Pressure. The apparatus used is a commercial high-pressure hydrogenator‡ having a bomb capable of being rocked mechanically under pressure. The bomb is equipped with a liner of glass or metal,§ which has a capacity of 250 ml. of reaction mixture. The bomb liner is fitted with a rubber stopper carrying a mechanical stirrer, inlet and outlet tubes for dry nitrogen, and a large buret or calibrated separatory funnel for addition of the Grignard reagent. The gas inlet hole in the side of the liner is closed with a piece of ordinary adhesive tape. Provision is made for the use of carbon monoxide under tank pressure (500 to 1000 p.s.i.); temperature control is unnecessary. The anhydrous chromium(III) chloride[6] is dried at 250° in an atmosphere of nitrogen and screened to 40 mesh after drying. The resulting powder is hygroscopic and should be kept out of contact with air as much as possible.

The liner is charged with 3.08 g. of dry chromium(III)

* Yale University, New Haven, Conn.
† Ethyl Corporation, Research Laboratories, Detroit, Mich.
‡ American Instrument Company 4⅜ in. series vessel No. 40622J.
§ Liners of glass, steel, and brass have been used successfully.

chloride and 60 ml. of anhydrous ether (dried over sodium). A solution of 27 g. (0.149 mol) phenylmagnesium bromide[7] in about 80 ml. of dry ether is introduced into the buret and kept under a nitrogen atmosphere.

The liner is now cooled in a Dry Ice–acetone bath to a temperature of about −70°. The stirrer is operated at about 200 to 300 r.p.m. to keep the chromium(III) chloride suspended evenly throughout the solution. A nitrogen atmosphere is maintained in the reaction vessel. At this temperature the Grignard reagent crystallizes from solution and little, if any, reaction takes place. The stirring apparatus is then detached; the liner is removed from the cooling bath, wiped quickly, closed, and inserted at once into the bomb of the hydrogenator. The bomb is sealed at once and placed under a pressure of carbon monoxide (500 to 1000 p.s.i.) and rocking is started. The yield of carbonyl depends to a large extent on getting the reaction mixture under a pressure of carbon monoxide before the contents of the liner reach a temperature of about −10°.

The bomb is rocked for about 2¾ hours, or for about 2 hours after the contents reach room temperature; longer periods are without effect on the yield of carbonyl. No heat is applied to the bomb and relatively little heat of reaction is observed under these conditions.

The carbon monoxide pressure is then released gradually and the contents of the liner transferred to a 3-l. flask containing ice water and 35 ml. of 5 N sulfuric acid. Additional ether is sometimes helpful in transferring the material from the reaction vessel to the flask; a good deal of heat is involved in the decomposition of the excess Grignard reagent at this point. The reaction mixture is now steam-distilled using an efficient condenser and a receiver cooled in ice and containing ice water. After the ether has been distilled over, crystals of carbonyl appear in the condenser and are gradually washed into the receiver by the distillate. It is sometimes necessary to increase the steam flow or decrease the flow of cooling water in the condenser to avoid clogging the outlet with crystals. Ether is added to the receiver to dissolve all the crystals and the ether layer separated, washed with water, and dried over anhydrous sodium sulfate. The ether is then distilled from the reaction product through a good fractionating column (about 15 theoretical plates); unless a column is used there is considerable loss of carbonyl by volatilization with the ether. Distillation is continued until the volume in the still pot is reduced to 50 ml.; the residue is then cooled in ice and the crystals filtered with suction. The product is washed with cold methanol and finally with a little cold ether and allowed to stand in air to dry.* The yield of practically pure, air-dried carbonyl is 1.95 to 2.2 g.† or 45 to 51 per cent of theory based on the amount of chromium(III) chloride employed.

Further purification of the carbonyl is effected by recrystallization from dry ether; this is best accomplished by placing the crude product in the thimble of a Soxhlet extractor and extracting with dry ether. Pure chromium hexacarbonyl crystallizes on cooling; it is filtered and washed as before.

A completely odorless product is obtained by sublimation of the recrystallized carbonyl at 0.5 mm. or less, and at a bath temperature of 40 to 50°; the large, highly refractive crystals are collected in a receiver cooled with Dry Ice. The sublimation apparatus must have a short, wide bore connection between the hot and cold sections to prevent clogging with crystals. The loss of product in the crystallization and sublimation processes is slight; several runs

* The drying in air should not be overdone, as the material is volatile at room temperature and is probably toxic. Loss of carbonyl may be incurred if the ethereal solutions are allowed to stand; a brownish deposit precipitates on standing overnight in the dark; decomposition in sunlight is rapid. There is also the possible hazard of violent decomposition if ethereal solutions are allowed to stand for extended periods. The authors have been advised by English workers that solutions of molybdenum hexacarbonyl have detonated on standing.

† Yields as high as 67 per cent have been obtained using the apparatus described here.

are conveniently combined for this operation. Larger scale bomb runs are limited by the capacity of the bomb and the additional time required in getting the mixture under pressure of carbon monoxide.

Procedure B

Preparation at Atmospheric Pressure. A 3-l. five-necked flask is equipped with a high-speed metal* stirrer, a condenser cooled with Dry Ice and acetone, a gas inlet tube for carbon monoxide, a thermometer, and a buret for delivering Grignard reagent. Provision is made for external cooling and the entire apparatus is set up in a good hood. A suspension of 12 g. of anhydrous chromium(III) chloride in 700 ml. of dry ether is stirred vigorously (5000 r.p.m.) and cooled to −70°. Without interrupting the stirring, 210 ml. of 2.7 N phenylmagnesium bromide is added over a period of 1 hour at this temperature. The Dry Ice cooling bath is then replaced with an ice-water bath and a rapid stream of carbon monoxide (220 l./hour) is led into the stirred mixture. The reaction begins at about −10° as indicated by the appearance of a dark color. The reaction is allowed to proceed for 15 to 30 minutes longer at a temperature not exceeding 0°. At the end of this time the mixture is poured into ice water containing 100 ml. of 6 N sulfuric acid, and the carbonyl isolated as described above for the high-pressure method. Typical yields will average 1.8 g. or 11 per cent of theoretical.†

Properties

Chromium hexacarbonyl forms large, highly refractive crystals that can be sublimed in vacuum without change but decompose on heating above about 100°. The vapor pressure of chromium hexacarbonyl has been measured up to 125°.[4] On exposure to light and air at room temperature

---

* The propeller used was gold-plated steel.

† Efficient stirring and a vigorous stream of carbon monoxide will help to achieve yields as high as 24 per cent.

in the impure solid state or in ether solution it decomposes slowly to a brown powder, but the pure solid can be preserved indefinitely out of direct sunlight. Chromium hexacarbonyl is soluble in ether, chloroform, and other organic solvents and insoluble in water and methanol.

References

1. JOB and CANAL: *Compt. rend.*, **183**, 392 (1926).
2. ANISSIMOC and NESMEYANOV: *Compt. rend. acad. sci. (U.S.S.R.)*, **26**, 58 (1940).
3. OWEN, ENGLISH, CASSIDY, and DUNDON: *J. Am. Chem. Soc.*, **69**, 1723 (1947).
4. HIEBER and ROMBERG: *Z. anorg. allgem. Chem.*, **221**, 321 (1935).
5. WINDSOR and BLANCHARD: *J. Am. Chem. Soc.*, **56**, 823 (1934).
6. HEISIG, FAWKES, and HEDIN: INORGANIC SYNTHESES, **2**, 193 (1946).
7. ALLEN and CONVERSE: "Organic Syntheses," Collective Vol. 1, 221 (1932).

43. POTASSIUM OCTACYANOMOLYBDATE(IV) 2-HYDRATE

(Potassium Molybdocyanide Dihydrate)

$$K_4Mo(CN)_8 \cdot 2H_2O$$

SUBMITTED BY N. H. FURMAN* AND C. O. MILLER*
CHECKED BY P. G. ARVAN† AND L. F. AUDRIETH†

Potassium octacyanomolybdate(IV) may be prepared by the action of potassium cyanide upon certain tri-, tetra-, or pentavalent derivatives of molybdenum. The latter are obtained by chemical[1-5] or electrochemical[6] reduction of molybdic acid.

The recommended procedure was first devised by Rosenheim[7] and later modified by Fieser.[8] The various steps in the synthesis cannot be represented by exact chemical equations but may be outlined diagrammatically as follows:

$$MoO_3 \xrightarrow[\text{HCl}]{\text{H}_2\text{O}} H_2MoO_4 \xrightarrow{\text{KSCN}} MoO_2(SCN)_3 \xrightarrow{\text{C}_5\text{H}_5\text{N}}$$

$$MoO_2(SCN)_3 \cdot 2C_5H_5N \xrightarrow{\text{KCN}} K_4Mo(CN)_8 \cdot 2H_2O$$

* Princeton University, Princeton, N.J.
† University of Illinois, Urbana, Ill.

Although not extremely efficient, this procedure is rapid and reliable, and requires no special apparatus or technique.

Procedure

Fifty grams (0.346 mol) of pure molybdenum(VI) oxide, MoO_3, is dissolved in a solution of 40 g. (0.714 mol) of potassium hydroxide in 100 ml. of water. To this solution is added 250 ml. of concentrated hydrochloric acid. The addition is made slowly and with constant stirring; the final solution is heated on a steam bath.

A concentrated solution of potassium thiocyanate is prepared by dissolving 150 g. (1.545 mol) of the salt in 150 ml. of water. This solution is added slowly and with constant stirring to the hot molybdic acid solution. The resulting deep red solution is diluted with 300 ml. of water and heated on a steam bath for 2 hours, with frequent stirring.

The solution is filtered while still warm and the filtrate transferred to a 2-l. beaker. Pyridine is added slowly and with constant stirring until a yellow solid begins to separate. About 65 to 75 ml. of pyridine will be required. The beaker is then placed in an ice bath until the red oily layer that has settled out on the bottom becomes very viscous. The supernatant liquid, which is still slightly red in color, is decanted and the product washed twice with water.

The oily liquid is treated with a solution of 200 g. (3.07 mols) of potassium cyanide in 300 ml. of water. Caution. *This step must be carried out in a well ventilated hood, as noxious gases are evolved.* The oily pyridine compound dissolves rapidly to give first a green and then a yellow-brown solution. This solution is heated on a steam bath, with frequent stirring, for ½ hour. A black by-product usually separates from the solution; it is removed by filtration (*hood*) and discarded. The filtrate is evaporated until its volume has been reduced 50 per cent. The concentrated solution is cooled in an ice bath, and the dark amber crystals collected on a Büchner funnel.

The crude product containing a considerable amount of a black contaminant is dissolved in a minimum amount of warm water (70°), treated with decolorizing charcoal (Darco), and filtered. To the filtrate is added slowly one to two volumes of ethyl alcohol until a golden-yellow crystalline solid separates. This purification process may be repeated if a product of higher purity is desired. The crystals are collected on a Büchner funnel, washed with alcohol, then ether,* and finally dried in a vacuum.

Further evaporation of the mother liquor yields only small amounts of the product, which becomes increasingly difficult to purify.

The yield is 75 to 85 g. of pure $K_4Mo(CN)_8 \cdot 2H_2O$ (44 to 50 per cent of the theoretical yield based on the molybdic oxide). Three careful recrystallizations will generally suffice to give a salt that, when titrated in dilute sulfuric acid against standard cerium(IV) sulfate using the o-phenanthroline–iron(II) complex or Erio Green (naphtalin green V) as indicator, will be found to be 100 per cent pure.

Properties

On heating at 110°, the potassium octacyanomolybdate(IV) 2-hydrate loses its water of hydration. The salt is extremely soluble in water, from which it may be crystallized in the form of yellow rhombic bipyramidal crystals, (a:b:c = 0.7028:1:0.3711). It is oxidized by cerium(IV) salt solution to the corresponding octacyanomolybdate(V), $K_3Mo(CN)_8$. Aqueous solutions are photosensitive and, on prolonged exposure to direct sunlight, turn red and then pale green with the evolution of hydrogen cyanide.

References

1. CHILESOTTI: Gazz. chim. ital., **34**, II, 493 (1904).
2. BUCKNALL and WARDLAW: J. Chem. Soc., 2983 (1927).
3. ROSENHEIM, GARFUNKEL, and KOHN: Z. anorg. Chem., **65**, 166 (1910).
4. JAKOB and TURKIEWICZ: Roczinki Chem., **11**, 569 (1931).
5. SAND and BURGER: Ber., **38**, 3384 (1905).

* The washing with ether is important if the anhydrous compound is to be prepared by subsequent drying at 100 to 110°.

6. WILLARD and THIELKE: *J. Am. Chem. Soc.*, **57**, 2609 (1935).
7. ROSENHEIM and KOSS: *Z. anorg. Chem.*, **49**, 148 (1906); ROSENHEIM: *ibid.*, **54**, 97 (1907).
8. FIESER: *J. Am. Chem. Soc.*, **52**, 5226 (1930).

44. TUNGSTEN(VI) CHLORIDE

(Tungsten Hexachloride)

$$WO_3 + 3H_2 \rightarrow W + 3H_2O$$
$$W + 3Cl_2 \rightarrow WCl_6$$

SUBMITTED BY M. H. LIETZKE* AND M. L. HOLT*
CHECKED BY A. J. VANDER WEYDEN† AND J. H. CALLISON†

Tungsten(VI) chloride has been prepared by heating tungsten(VI) oxide and phosphorus(V) chloride in a sealed tube,[1,2] and by the action of chlorine on powdered tungsten metal.[3,4] The latter method is preferred because it permits the removal of molybdenum impurities from the tungsten and also because it avoids the separation of phosphorus(V) oxychloride from tungsten(VI) chloride that is required in the other method. Since the tungsten metal powder commercially available is rather impure, it is desirable to prepare it as needed by reducing tungsten(VI) oxide with hydrogen.

Apparatus

The apparatus shown in Fig. 29 is suitable for this preparation. A sillimanite tube *A* about 2 ft. long and with an internal diameter of about 1 in. serves as the reaction tube. It is placed in an electric furnace that will give a temperature of about 1000°. To one end of the sillimanite tube is fused a piece of pyrex tubing *B* attached in turn to two flasks *C* and *D* with vertical tubes in which refluxing and purification of the product are accomplished. The flask *D* is sealed to a piece of tubing *E* that passes through a two-hole stopper into a 500-ml. Erlenmeyer flask *F* containing concentrated sodium hydroxide solution. The tube

* University of Wisconsin, Madison, Wis.
† University of Denver, Denver, Colo.

E should terminate just above the surface of the sodium hydroxide solution to avoid the possibility of being plugged with reaction products. The exit tube from the flask should lead to a fume hood.

The other end of the sillimanite tube is fitted with a one-hole stopper and connected by means of a two-way glass stopcock *G* with two pairs of wash bottles, *H* and *I*, containing concentrated sulfuric acid. It is advisable to connect a glass tube *J*, containing copper turnings heated by a small electric furnace (about 500°), to the pair of bottles *I* to remove oxygen from the nitrogen. The purification train *I* is used exclusively for hydrogen or nitrogen and the train *H* for chlorine only.

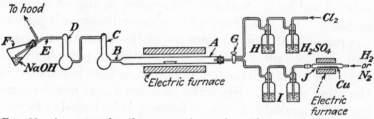

FIG. 29. Apparatus for the preparation and purification of tungsten(VI) chloride.

Procedure

A 7½-g. sample of tungsten(VI) oxide is ignited in a platinum crucible for an hour using a Méker burner. The product is allowed to cool and then transferred to a porcelain combustion boat after which the boat and contents are placed in the sillimanite tube in the furnace. While the furnace is heating gradually to 1000°, hydrogen is passed slowly through the train *I* without using the small furnace. Reduction of the tungsten(VI) oxide takes place as indicated by droplets of water that condense in the glass tube outside the furnace. The water should be displaced from the system by heating the walls with a free flame. Complete reduction is indicated when no more water forms; the furnace is then turned off. The stream of hydrogen should be continued until the furnace has cooled to nearly room temperature (several hours). The hydrogen in the system is then displaced by passing nitrogen through the same train I with the smaller furnace operating. After about 30 minutes the nitrogen is turned off and chlorine admitted to the reaction tube through the train H. The chlorine should be allowed to flow for about 15 minutes before the larger furnace is turned on. Small amounts of reddish-orange tungsten(VI) oxychlorides (WO_2Cl_2 and $WOCl_4$) may form at first, but are easily displaced completely from the tube by heating with a burner. Reaction to produce tungsten(VI) chloride starts at about 600°. The blue-black tungsten(VI) chloride deposits in shining crystals in the tube outside the furnace. Reaction is complete after about 2 hours. The tungsten(VI) chloride is then sublimed into flask C. Since molybdenum(V) chloride is more volatile (b.p. 260°) than tungsten(VI) chloride, its separation is effected in this step. The crystals that condense in the second flask D contain most of the molybdenum(V) chloride. After the tungsten(VI) chloride has been sublimed into the collecting flask, the flow of chlorine is stopped and the constrictions are sealed off. A new bulb system can then be sealed to the glass tube B and the apparatus prepared for another run. In a typical experiment 8.85 g. of tungsten(VI) chloride was obtained corresponding to a 69 per cent yield.

Properties

Tungsten(VI) chloride is a blue-black crystalline substance with a bluish-violet tinge. It melts at 275° and boils at 346°. At low temperatures, *e.g.*, in an acetone–Dry Ice bath, it becomes wine-red in color. When tungsten(VI) chloride vapor is cooled rapidly, it condenses to the red form, which is easily converted to the black form upon gentle heating. Tungsten(VI) chloride is readily hydrolyzed, even in moist air.   It is soluble in carbon disulfide, carbon tetrachloride, and phosphorus(V) oxychloride.

References

1. TECLU: *Ann.*, **187**, 255 (1877).
2. KETELAAR and VAN OOSTERHOUT: *Rec. trav. chim.*, **62**, 197 and 597 (1943).
3. HÖNIGSCHMID and MENN: *Z. anorg. allgem. Chem.*, **229**, 49 (1936).
4. SMITH and EXNER: *Chem. News*, **90**, 66 (1904).

45. URANIUM(IV) OXALATE

$$UO_2(C_2H_3O_2)_2 + 4HCl + Na_2S_2O_4$$
$$\rightarrow UCl_4 + 2NaHSO_3 + 2HC_2H_3O_2$$
$$UCl_4 + 2H_2C_2O_4 + 6H_2O$$
$$\rightarrow U(C_2O_4)_2 \cdot 6H_2O + 4HCl$$

SUBMITTED BY LOUIS E. MARCHI[*]
CHECKED BY W. C. FERNELIUS[†] AND GORDON S. DOUGLAS[†]

Uranium(IV) oxalate has been prepared by the reaction of uranium(IV) chloride,[1-3] sulfate,[4,5] and hydroxide[6] with a saturated solution of oxalic acid, or by the reduction of a water-soluble uranyl compound with copper,[7] zinc,[7] or sodium dithionite $(Na_2S_2O_4)$,[4,7] followed by treatment with oxalic acid.   It is prepared conveniently by the reduction of the readily available uranyl acetate 2-hydrate with sodium dithionite.

The reduction of the uranyl ion by the dithionite ion in acid solution may be assumed to take place substantially in accordance with the following equations:

$$UO_2{}^{++} + 4H^+ + 2e^- + 6Cl^- \rightarrow UCl_6{}^= + 2H_2O$$
$$\underline{S_2O_4{}^= + 2H_2O \rightarrow 2HSO_3{}^- + 2H^+ + 2e^-}$$
$$UO_2{}^{++} + 2H^+ + S_2O_4{}^= + 6Cl^- \rightarrow UCl_6{}^= + 2HSO_3{}^-$$

However, some colloidal sulfur is also formed, possibly because of the following side reactions:[8]

[*] University of Pittsburgh, Pittsburgh, Pa.
[†] Purdue University, Lafayette, Ind.

$$2S_2O_4^= + H_2O \rightarrow S_2O_3^= + 2HSO_3^-$$
$$S_2O_3^= + 2H^+ \rightarrow H_2O + SO_2 + S$$

Consequently, twice the amount of dithionite calculated from the above equation is used to ensure complete reduction.

Procedure

Five grams (0.012 mol) of powdered uranyl acetate 2-hydrate is dissolved in 100 ml. of warm (80°) dilute hydrochloric acid (10 ml. of concentrated hydrochloric acid and 90 ml. of water). Five grams (0.024 mol) of powdered sodium dithionite 2-hydrate is added in small amounts while the solution is stirred. As the dithionite comes in contact with the solution a brown material is formed that quickly changes to a whitish-green precipitate. Five milliliters of concentrated hydrochloric acid is added and the mixture is then heated on a steam bath for at least 10 minutes until solution has been effected. The solution is usually cloudy due to the formation and presence of a small amount of free sulfur. The latter is easily removed by filtration, yielding a filtrate that possesses the characteristic dark green color of the uranium(IV) ion.

Since the uranium(IV) ion is very readily oxidized in solution by atmospheric oxygen, the warm (60°) dark green solution is treated immediately with 20 ml. of a saturated solution of oxalic acid 2-hydrate. Slow addition of the reagent with good stirring yields a heavy, compact, gray precipitate that settles to the bottom of the vessel after a few minutes. After standing for ½ hour, the precipitated uranium(IV) oxalate will have changed to a dark green color. It is washed at least five times by decantation with 100-ml. portions of water, or until the supernatant liquid gives no further test for hydrogen sulfite ion (by the addition of 5 ml. of 0.25 M barium chloride, 1 ml. of dilute hydrochloric acid (1:1), and 5 drops of 0.1 N potassium permanganate to 10 ml. of supernatant liquid) and for oxalate ion (by the addition of 5 ml. of 0.25 M barium chloride to another 10-ml. sample of supernatant liquid). The precipitate is separated by filtration and air-dried, since it is not oxidized by atmospheric oxygen. The yield, based on the quantity of uranyl acetate, is 5.7 g. (99 per cent).

Properties

Uranium(IV) oxalate 6-hydrate commonly crystallizes in dark green microcrystals, which are not reactive toward the water vapor and oxygen of the air, in contrast to the rapid atmospheric oxidation of solutions of uranium(IV) ion. Four molecules of water are lost when the compound is dried in a vacuum at room temperature. When uranium(IV) oxalate 6-hydrate is heated to 100 to 110°, five molecules of water are lost; the sixth is lost at 200°. The anhydrous compound is blue-violet.

The compound is only slightly soluble in water and dilute acids but is soluble in warm concentrated hydrochloric acid to form a dark green solution. It can be reprecipitated by cooling or by diluting such a solution. Concentrated nitric acid effects oxidation to the uranyl salt. With solutions of the alkali carbonates or hydrogen carbonates, uranium(IV) hydroxide is formed. With an excess of a solution of potassium carbonate and by atmospheric oxidation, potassium uranyl carbonate results. Uranium(IV) oxalate 6-hydrate is also soluble in solutions of alkali and ammonium oxalates to form the tetraoxalatouranate(IV) ion.

References

1. Péligot: Ann. chim. phys., [3] **5**, 5 (1842); Ann., **43**, 255 (1842).
2. Rammelsberg: Pogg. Ann., **59**, 1 (1843).
3. Kohlschütter: Ber., **34**, 3619 (1901).
4. Aloy and Auber: Bull. soc. chim., [4] **1**, 569 (1907).
5. Rosenheim and Kelmy: Z. anorg. allgem. Chem., **206**, 33 (1932).
6. Aloy: Bull. soc. chim., [3] **21**, 615 (1899).
7. Kohlschütter and Rossi: Ber., **34**, 1472 (1901).
8. Latimer: "The Oxidation States of the Elements and Their Potentials in Aqueous Solutions," p. 69, Prentice-Hall, Inc., New York, 1938.

46. POTASSIUM TETRAOXALATOURANATE(IV)

$$U(C_2O_4)_2 \cdot 6H_2O + 2K_2C_2O_4 \cdot H_2O$$
$$\rightarrow K_4U(C_2O_4)_4 \cdot 5H_2O + 3H_2O$$

SUBMITTED BY LOUIS E. MARCHI[*]
CHECKED BY W. C. FERNELIUS[†] AND GORDON S. DOUGLAS[†]

Potassium tetraoxalatouranate(IV) 5-hydrate has been prepared by the reaction of a potassium oxalate solution with an excess of uranium(IV) oxalate 6-hydrate.[1-3] This excess prevents contamination of the product by potassium oxalate, since both potassium tetraoxalatouranate(IV) and potassium oxalate are precipitated from aqueous solution by absolute alcohol.

Procedure

A solution of 5 g. (0.027 mol) of potassium oxalate 1-hydrate in 20 ml. of water is added to a slurry of 6 g. (0.014 mol) of uranium(IV) oxalate 6-hydrate in 50 ml. of water. The reaction is complete after the mixture has been heated on a steam bath for 1 hour. The dark green filtrate is treated with 200 ml. of absolute alcohol, which is added drop by drop from a separatory funnel while the mixture is stirred.[‡] Small light green crystals are obtained, which are quickly dried by washing them several times with absolute alcohol and finally with ether. To avoid oxidation, potassium tetraoxalatouranate(IV) is stored in a desiccator over phosphorus(V) oxide.

Properties

At 17° the solubility[3] of potassium tetraoxalatouranate(IV) 5-hydrate is 21.73 g. per 100 g. of water. The salt is only very slightly soluble in alcohol-water mixtures. Addition of barium ions to water solutions results in

* University of Pittsburgh, Pittsburgh, Pa.
† Purdue University, Lafayette, Ind.
‡ The alcohol must not be added too rapidly, or a gummy product that adheres tenaciously to the walls of the vessel will form.

formation of barium tetraoxalatouranate(IV) 9-hydrate, $Ba_2[U(C_2O_4)_4]\cdot 9H_2O$, but with calcium and strontium ions the 8-hydrates of the mixed salts, $K_2Ca[U(C_2O_4)_4]\cdot 8H_2O$ and $K_2Sr[U(C_2O_4)_4]\cdot 8H_2O$, are formed. Silver ions are reduced to metallic silver by an aqueous solution of potassium tetraoxalatouranate(IV).

Dehydration of $K_4[U(C_2O_4)_4]\cdot 5H_2O$ at 200° for several hours yields the 1-hydrate; longer heating (for several days) at this temperature causes decomposition and oxidation.

References

1. KOHLSCHÜTTER and ROSSI: *Ber.*, **34**, 1474 (1901).
2. KOHLSCHÜTTER: *ibid.*, 3630 (1901).
3. ORLOW: *J. Russ. Phys. Chem. Soc.*, **34**, 375 (1902).

CHAPTER VII

47. ANHYDROUS METAL FLUORIDES

SUBMITTED BY HOMER F. PRIEST*
CHECKED BY CARL F. SWINEHART†

The preparation of anhydrous fluorides, and particularly the preparation of higher-valent anhydrous fluorides, presents many unique problems both with regard to the special apparatus required and in the handling of the compounds themselves.

The literature contains many preparative methods utilizing anhydrous hydrogen fluoride as the reactant with chlorides or oxides. While anhydrous fluorides are produced in many cases by such methods, they are frequently, if not always, contaminated with varying amounts of

* Massachusetts Institute of Technology, Cambridge, Mass.
† Harshaw Chemical Company, Cleveland, Ohio.

hydrogen fluoride held by coordination, adsorption, or chemisorption. Furthermore, the "bifluoride" type of compound, such as KF·HF, is formed readily with many fluorides other than the alkali fluorides. For these reasons, anhydrous hydrogen fluoride is not used in the specific procedures that follow, even for the preparation of fluorides of lower valence that may serve as the starting materials for the higher valent compounds. In all cases the fluorine is supplied as elementary fluorine.

It is assumed that a supply of fluorine will be available, prepared as described by Simons[1] or Cady.[2] If desired, a small electrolytic generating unit can be purchased ready for operation,[3] or the gas may be obtained in cylinders.[4] A flow of at least 150 ml./min. will be required in the preparations to follow. It is best to remove traces of hydrogen fluoride from the fluorine by means of a cold trap in Dry Ice, followed by a nickel absorption tube containing anhydrous sodium fluoride pellets, maintained at 100°.*

A very satisfactory general type of reactor, constructed of either nickel or Monel, is shown in Fig. 30. This unit is suitable for all the preparations to be described, as well as for many others involving use of either fluorine or anhydrous hydrogen fluoride. Modifications may be made, but most of the design features are the result of considerable experience; deviations, particularly by inexperienced workers, should be made with caution. It is well to use nickel tubing with silver-soldered joints for connections, although copper may also be used. Hoke blunt-point brass needle valves are satisfactory wherever valves are indicated, unless otherwise specified.

The reactants should be put in the reactor in a tray made by splitting a 10-in. length of ½-in. nickel tubing lengthwise and spreading it open as far as possible while retaining a loose fit in the reactor.

Fluorine may safely be bubbled through 98 per cent

* Porous absorbent pellets of sodium fluoride made for this purpose are obtainable from the Harshaw Chemical Company, Cleveland, Ohio.

sulfuric acid to provide pressure releases or atmospheric seals. If glass seals are used they should be attached to the metal system with copper-to-glass Housekeeper seals.* Hydrogen fluoride, fluorine, and some metal fluorides produce painful burns when in contact with the flesh. Care should be taken to prevent burns, but if any result acci-

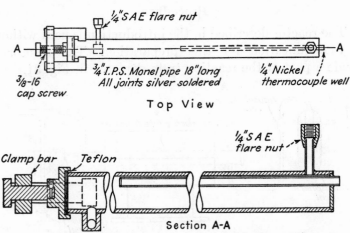

Top View

Section A-A

Fig. 30. Metal reactor for carrying out fluorination reactions.

dentally, they should be treated by prolonged soaking with lime water or dilute ammonia. If white blisters form, the blister tissue must be removed and the tissue under the blister treated with a mild reactant, such as boric acid or milk of magnesia. Ice packs will reduce the pain of fluoride burns. As with all chemical burns, immediate flushing with quantities of water is the first and best preliminary treatment to use (see also synthesis 29).

A. NICKEL(II) FLUORIDE

$$NiCl_2 + F_2 \rightarrow NiF_2 + Cl_2$$

While nickel fluoride is not to be classed as a higher-valent fluoride, it is nevertheless the only nickel fluoride

* General Electric Company, Schenectady, N.Y.

that has been definitely characterized.[8] The procedure detailed below represents an excellent example of the method to be used for the preparation of a simple type of anhydrous fluoride. Few complications arise. The product may be handled without difficulty since anhydrous nickel fluoride is nonhygroscopic when prepared in this manner.

Procedure

The reactor described in the introduction is used without any modification for this preparation. The reactor is made a part of the reaction train depicted in Fig. 31.

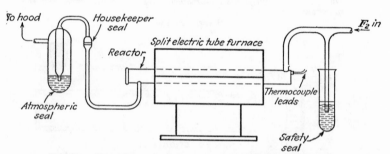

FIG. 31.   Reaction train for preparation of nickel(II) fluoride.

Fifty grams of hydrated nickel chloride is dried in a porcelain dish at 350° in a muffle furnace. Some hydrolysis takes place but contamination of the material with nickel oxide does not interfere with the reaction because nickel oxide reacts fairly rapidly with fluorine. The dried nickel chloride is ground to pass a 30-mesh screen and spread in the nickel reaction tray in as thin a layer as possible.

The loaded tray is placed in the reactor and fluorine passed over the nickel chloride while the temperature of the furnace is raised to 350°. After 3 hours at this temperature (or when twice the calculated amount of fluorine, estimated from the known rate of production of the fluorine generator and the time, has passed over the sample), the effluent gases are tested for chlorine by bubbling the gas through dilute alkali for 1 minute only, acidifying with nitric acid, and adding silver nitrate. Flow of fluorine is continued for 1 hour after a negative chlorine test is obtained. After cooling in the fluorine stream, the system is purged with nitrogen and the product removed as a homogeneous, pale yellow powder. The product should be kept in a desiccator until used. The yield is practically theoretical, 18 to 19 g. being obtained as product.

Properties

Nickel fluoride is a light yellow, homogeneous powder, nonhygroscopic unless mixed with hydrated nickel fluoride, insoluble in water but soluble in dilute ammonium hydroxide.

B. COBALT(III) FLUORIDE

$$2CoCl_2 + 3F_2 \rightarrow 2CoF_3 + 2Cl_2$$

Cobalt(III) fluoride has been found to be a useful fluorinating agent in the production of fluorocarbons;[5] it can be used for a variety of fluorinating reactions as a substitute for elementary fluorine. While it is not possible to obtain elementary fluorine by heating cobalt(III) fluoride, it can be used to prepare higher-valent volatile fluorides that could not otherwise be obtained except by the use of elementary fluorine. The method of preparation described here is similar to that used by Ruff and his coworkers.[6]

Procedure

A reactor set up exactly like the one used in the preparation of anhydrous nickel fluoride is needed.

Fifty grams of hydrated cobalt(II) chloride is heated in a porcelain dish until the compound is completely dehydrated. Hydrolysis with attendant formation of black cobalt oxide will cause no difficulty. The hot cobalt(II) chloride is transferred to a hot porcelain mortar and ground to a uniform powder as rapidly as possible. After grinding, the material is transferred to the nickel reactor tray, and the tray is placed in the reactor. It is advisable, but not essential, to have dry nitrogen flowing through the reactor during the insertion of the tray and its contents.

The flow of fluorine is started, and the furnace is heated to 250° and maintained at this temperature for 3 hours after a test for chlorine has shown the latter to be absent from the exit gas. The fluorine is then purged from the system with dry nitrogen in preparation for the removal of the product. A metal can with a tight-fitting snap lid is cleaned and dried; air in the container is displaced completely by dry nitrogen. The container is then placed beside the reactor containing the cobalt(III) fluoride. The reactor closure is removed, the tray is withdrawn, and the product transferred to the can as rapidly as possible* (1 to 3 seconds being adequate), after which the container is capped.

The product is a light brown solid that fumes and turns dark brown in moist air. It is easily handled in a dry box and may be analyzed either for the elements or, as is more common, for available fluorine using iodometric methods. The yield will vary from 22 to 23 g. (90 to 95 per cent of theory).

Properties

Cobalt(III) fluoride is a light brown powder that appears to be amorphous upon examination. In moist air it undergoes hydrolysis with formation of hydrogen fluoride and turns dark brown. It reacts violently with water and with hydrocarbons. When stored in an airtight metal container it is quite stable and may be kept for extended periods of time. Its density is 3.89 g./ml. at 18°.

C. SILVER(II) FLUORIDE

$$AgCl + F_2 \rightarrow AgF_2 + \tfrac{1}{2}Cl_2$$

Silver(II) fluoride[9] is an excellent fluorinating agent, although not as generally useful as is cobalt(III) fluoride.

---

* Speed is essential and is a satisfactory substitute for a "dry box."

Silver(II) fluoride reacts more vigorously with most substances than does cobalt(III) fluoride and is therefore more difficult to handle. It is also more hygroscopic and must be kept in a dry atmosphere at all times.

Procedure

Fifty grams of freshly precipitated silver chloride is dried overnight at 110°, ground to pass a 30-mesh sieve, and then spread in a thin layer in the reaction tray. The latter is placed in the reactor and subjected to the action of fluorine at a furnace temperature of 200°. Fluorine is passed over the material in the tray until no trace of chlorine is found in the exit gas, and then for an additional 3 hours. The fluorine is swept out with dry nitrogen and the product removed using either the technique described under the preparation of cobalt(III) fluoride or the more satisfactory procedure that is described in detail in the following paragraph.

A glass tube, of the same diameter as the reactor tube and with a side arm sealed on in the middle, is connected by means of the side arm to a source of dry nitrogen and thoroughly flushed. With nitrogen flowing through the reactor and through the glass transfer tube, the reactor is opened and the transfer tube placed against the reactor opening; the tray with its contents is drawn into the glass transfer tube, which is then stoppered and placed in a dry box while under positive pressure. In the dry box the silver(II) fluoride is transferred to a snap-lid metal can.

Based on available fluorine, a yield of 90 to 95 per cent of theory (45 to 48 g.) is obtained by the foregoing procedure.

Properties

Silver(II) fluoride is a gray-black, amorphous solid frequently showing a yellow bloom. It reacts very vigorously with water and is very hygroscopic, being converted to a greasy black mass by exposure to atmospheric moisture.

D. CARBON TETRAFLUORIDE

$$SiC + 4F_2 \rightarrow CF_4 + SiF_4$$

Carbon tetrafluoride is an extremely stable gas at room temperature and hence is suitable for applications calling for a stable gas of higher molecular weight than can be obtained by use of the inexpensive inert gases of the atmosphere. The method of preparation described here gives a product of high purity without attendant explosion hazards such as present themselves in the direct fluorination of carbon.

Procedure

The nickel reactor is used to carry out this synthesis. One hundred grams of 30-mesh Carborundum is distributed uniformly along the tray; 1 to 2 g. of silicon metal powder is mixed with the charge at the end of the tray where the fluorine enters the reactor. The silicon serves to effect ignition of the charge. The reactor is closed and the outlet is connected to a trap constructed as shown in Fig. 32. A sulfuric acid safety bubbler and atmospheric seal is connected to the exit of the trap.

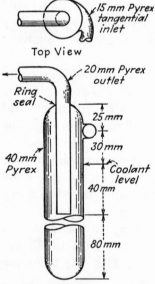

Fig. 32. Trap for condensation of carbon tetrafluoride.

The flow of fluorine is started and as soon as the reaction has commenced, as indicated by heating of the reactor, the fluorine is diluted with an equal volume of dry nitrogen. When a good flow of product is obtained, as evidenced by copious fumes at the exit, the trap is cooled in liquid nitrogen to condense the silicon tetrafluoride and carbon tetrafluoride. The reaction is allowed to continue until the desired amount of product has been formed and condensed. The fluorine utilization is nearly quantitative, so the rate of supply of fluorine can serve as an index of the quantity of product being formed. When the reaction is complete, the trap is disconnected from the reactor and is then connected to a purification train consisting of three gas-washing bottles containing 20 per cent sodium hydroxide solution, followed by a drying tower filled with Drierite. The contents of the trap are allowed to warm to volatilize the mixture, and the gases pass through the washing train where removal of the silicon tetrafluoride is effected by hydrolysis. The exit gas from the third bottle is carbon tetrafluoride of high purity and may be condensed or stored in a gasometer.

Properties

Carbon tetrafluoride is a colorless, tasteless, and odorless gas when pure but may have a musty odor if contaminated with some of the higher fluorocarbons. It boils at $-128°$ and is inert to hydrolysis of any kind except at temperatures above 1000°. It is inert toward most chemicals although boiling alkali metals and superheated alkali metal vapors attack it slowly.

E. TANTALUM(NIOBIUM)(V) FLUORIDE

[Tantalum (Niobium) Pentafluoride]

$$2Ta + 5F_2 \rightarrow 2TaF_5$$
$$2Nb + 5F_2 \rightarrow 2NbF_5$$

Owing to the fact that tantalum and niobium pentafluorides sublime at temperatures above 200°, it is necessary to use a slightly different technique in their preparation. The procedure described here is, however, applicable to a wide variety of fluoride preparations.

Procedure

The fluoride reactor described in the introduction should be modified by replacing the $\frac{1}{4}$-in. tube used in the other

preparations with a ½-in. Monel tube at the exit. A trap
is constructed as shown in Fig. 33

Top View

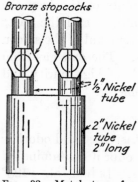

FIG. 33. Metal trap for
condensation of tantalum-
(niobium)(V) fluoride.

and the apparatus is assembled as
shown in Fig. 34. The heating wire
is asbestos-covered Nichrome,
wound so that the region from the
exit of the reactor to the chamber
of the trap can be maintained at
300°.

The tray is charged with 50 g. of
tantalum or niobium powder and
the flow of fluorine is started. It
may be necessary to raise the temperature of the furnace as high as
300° to initiate the reaction, but
that is normally unnecessary. The
line heater should be placed in operation to prevent clogging of the
line. The trap is cooled to within
1 in. of the inlet tube with ice and
water. The reaction is continued
until fluorine is detected at the exit, after which the flow
of fluorine is stopped and the valves on the trap closed.

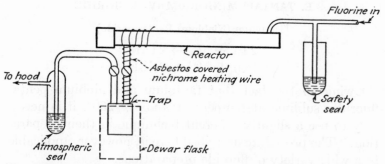

Fig. 34. Apparatus assembly for preparation and purification of tantalum-
(niobium)(V) fluoride.

It is desirable, although not essential, to purge the system
first with dry nitrogen.

The trap is frozen in Dry Ice–trichloroethylene slush and pumped free of noncondensables by means of a Hyvac pump, after which the tantalum(V) fluoride [or niobium(V) fluoride] may be readily sublimed into the reactor or container where it is to be used.

Properties

Niobium(V) fluoride[10,11] and tantalum(V) fluoride[12,13] are white, crystalline solids, both of which boil at 229° and melt at 75° and 97° respectively. They form a eutectic mixture that is liquid at room temperature. Both compounds must be handled under anhydrous conditions since they are hygroscopic and fume in moist air. Niobium(V) fluoride and tantalum(V) fluoride have specific gravities of 3.29 and 4.74 respectively.

F. TUNGSTEN(VI) FLUORIDE

(Tungsten Hexafluoride)

$$W + 3F_2 \rightarrow WF_6$$

Tungsten(VI) fluoride, with a molecular weight of 297.92, is one of the heaviest gases known and as such would be expected to have some interesting uses. Its reactive character may detract from possible applications, but where this property would not interfere the compound could be used. It was prepared and characterized by Ruff and his coworkers, who used the hexachloride as a starting material.[7] The method of direct synthesis used in the following procedure has proved to be very satisfactory and simple.[14]

Procedure

The nickel reactor already described (Fig. 30) and two traps, constructed as shown in Fig. 35, are needed for this preparation. The complete setup is shown in Fig. 36.

Fifty grams of tungsten metal powder is placed in the reactor tray in as thin a layer as possible. The tray is placed in the reactor, which is then closed, and the flow of fluorine is started; after a few minutes the reactor at the inlet end should become quite hot. The traps are cooled in a Dry Ice–trichloroethylene slush, which will condense all the product, so that no bubbling should take place at the exit atmospheric seal.

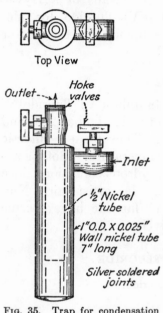

Top View

Outlet---

Hoke valves

←Inlet

½" Nickel tube

1" O.D. X 0.025" Wall nickel tube 7" long

Silver soldered joints

FIG. 35. Trap for condensation of tungsten(VI) fluoride.

If the fluorine is contaminated with oxygen, as it frequently is, the tube between the reactor and the first trap may plug with tungsten(VI) oxyfluoride, WOF_4, after the reaction has been running for a while. This plug may be removed by heating, which will effect sublimation of this material into the first trap. If, however, it is desired to have pure tungsten(VI) fluoride, it is best to stop the reaction if blocking occurs. The

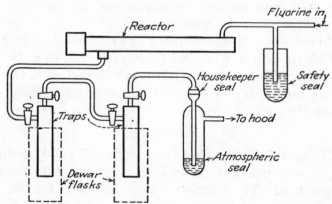

FIG. 36. Complete apparatus assembly for preparation of tungsten(VI) fluoride.

valves on the traps should then be closed and the traps disconnected. If blocking does not occur, the reaction is continued until the presence of fluorine is detected at the exit of the atmospheric seal, which indicates that all of the tungsten has undergone reaction. The fluorine flow should be stopped, the valves on the traps should be closed, and the traps disconnected.

The traps are frozen in a Dry Ice–trichloroethylene slush and evacuated with a Hyvac pump to remove the fluorine present. The product may be distilled from one container to another through evacuated lines. The traps serve admirably as storage cylinders for the material.

Properties

Tungsten(VI) fluoride is a colorless gas that condenses to a colorless liquid at 19.5° and freezes to a crystalline white solid at 2.5°. It fumes in moist air and must be handled under anhydrous conditions. The specific gravity of the liquid is 3.441 at 15°. It may be handled in carefully out-gassed glass systems provided that greases, mercury, and organic materials, as well as water, are absent from the system.

References

1. SIMONS: INORGANIC SYNTHESES, **1**, 138 (1939).
2. CADY: *ibid.*, **1**, 142 (1939).
3. Harshaw Chemical Company, Cleveland, Ohio.
4. Pennsylvania Salt Company, Philadelphia, Pa.
5. FOWLER and BURFORD: "Fluorocarbons," O.T.S. Report, Department of Commerce, Washington, D.C., 1947.
6. RUFF and ASCHER: *Z. anorg. allgem. Chem.*, **183**, 195 (1929).
7. RUFF, EUNER, and HELLER: *ibid.*, **52**, 256 (1907).
8. POULENC: *Compt. rend.*, **114**, 746, 1426 (1892).
9. RUFF and GIESE: *Ber.*, **69B**, 598 (1936).
10. MOISSAN: *Compt. rend.*, **66**, 180 (1868).
11. RUFF and ZEDNER: *Ber.*, **42**, 492 (1909).
12. MOISSAN: *Bull. soc. chim.*, [3] **27**, 434 (1902).
13. RUFF and SCHILLER: *Z. anorg. Chem.*, **72**, 355 (1911).
14. PRIEST and SCHUMB: *J. Am. Chem. Soc.*, **76**, 3378 (1948).

48. BROMINE(III) FLUORIDE

(Bromine Trifluoride)

$$Br_2 + 3F_2 \rightarrow 2BrF_3$$

SUBMITTED BY J. H. SIMONS*
CHECKED BY DON M. YOST† AND M. T. ROGERS†

The interhalogen compound bromine(III) fluoride has been prepared by (1) uniting a stream of gaseous fluorine with one of nitrogen-containing bromine vapor, and (2) bubbling fluorine through liquid bromine in a copper container. The latter procedure is preferred, since it is more readily controlled and makes possible production of bromine(III) fluoride in any desired quantity.

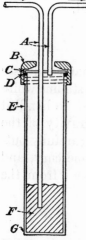

FIG. 37. Apparatus for the preparation of bromine (III) fluoride.

Procedure

The apparatus is shown in Fig. 37. The copper tubes *A* are silver-soldered to the copper cover disk *C*. To facilitate distillation of the product, these copper tubes should be silver-soldered at the outer ends to 7/25 copper tapers. Graphite is used as a lubricant. *B* is a brass cap which is drilled out to accommodate the copper tubes and which screws onto the copper vessel *E*. *D* is a fuse wire, Teflon, or similar gasket. The bottom of the copper reactor at *G* is welded to the walls of the copper container, since bromine trifluoride reacts readily with ordinary solders and brazing alloys.

Fluorine is prepared electrolytically either by the high-temperature process[2] or by electrolysis of $KF \cdot 2HF$ at 100°.[3] It is freed from hydrogen fluoride by passage through a tube

* Pennsylvania State College, State College, Pa.
† California Institute of Technology, Pasadena, Calif.

containing sodium fluoride or potassium fluoride at 100°, and then through a Dry Ice trap. The purified gas is bubbled through bromine in the copper vessel until fluorine escapes in quantity from the exit tube. The product may be retained in the reaction vessel by replacing *C* with a copper disk to close the vessel. Preferably, the bromine(III) fluoride is distilled from the reaction vessel at 1-cm. pressure into a platinum trap or a thoroughly dry and clean steel cylinder.*

Properties

Bromine(III) fluoride is an extremely reactive, straw-colored liquid at room temperature. It reacts rapidly with glass and most siliceous materials. The reaction with quartz is noticeable at 30°. It will set fire to materials like wood and paper. It reacts violently with water and with many organic substances. A small quantity frozen at −80°, when dropped into liquid toluene at the same temperature, reacts with great violence.

Bromine(III) fluoride melts at 8.8°[1] and boils at 127 ± 1°.[6] The critical temperature is about 327°.[1] The density of the solid at the melting point is 3.23 g./ml.; of the liquid, 2.843 g./ml.[1] The density of the liquid at any temperature can be calculated from the equation: $d = 3.623 - 0.00277T$.[1] The vapor pressure of the liquid follows the equation: $\log p = 8.41954 \dfrac{2220.2}{T}$. The heat of vaporization is about 10 kcal.[6] Calculations have given a value of 25.3 for Trouton's constant.[6]

References

1. Ruff and Braida: *Z. anorg. allgem. Chem.*, **206**, 63 (1932).
2. Simons: Inorganic Syntheses, **1**, 138 (1939).

* Other fluorides of bromine may be present as impurities: BrF, boiling at about 20°, and BrF_5, boiling at 40.5°. Since these are more volatile than the trifluoride, they are readily removed by distillation. If the fluorine is allowed to pass through the reaction mixture until the excess escapes from the exit tube, only negligible amounts of BrF will be present. As BrF_5[5] is formed in quantity only at 200°, it will be present in relatively small amounts.

3. Schumb, Young, and Radimer: *Ind. Eng. Chem.*, **39**, 243 (1947).
4. Ruff and Braida: *Z. anorg. allgem. Chem.*, **214**, 81 (1933).
5. Ruff and Menzel: *ibid.*, **202**, 49 (1931).
6. Ruff and Braida: *ibid.*, **214**, 91 (1933).

49. RHENIUM(VI) OXIDE

(Rhenium Trioxide)

Rhenium(VI) oxide can be prepared by the incomplete combustion of rhenium in oxygen, but the reaction is hard to control. It can also be obtained by the reduction of rhenium(VII) oxide (1) with rhenium at elevated temperatures[1] and (2) with rhenium(IV) oxide[2] at 300°. These procedures are unsatisfactory, as difficulty is experienced in removing unreacted rhenium or rhenium(VII) oxide. Simpler procedures that lead directly to pure products involve reducing rhenium(VII) oxide with either dioxane or carbon monoxide.

Procedure A

$$Re_2O_7 + xC_4H_8O_2 \rightarrow Re_2O_7 \cdot (C_4H_8O_2)_x$$
$$Re_2O_7 \cdot (C_4H_8O_2)_x \xrightarrow{125-145°} ReO_3 + \text{decomposition product}$$

Submitted by H. Nechamkin* and C. F. Hiskey*
Checked by Therald Moeller† and C. E. Shoemaker†

The reaction tube containing approximately 1 g. of rhenium(VII) oxide (synthesis 50) is detached from the apparatus. Four milliliters of anhydrous dioxane, dried by distillation from sodium metal, is poured over the sample, the operation being performed rapidly to reduce moisture pickup. The reaction tube is then warmed gently to dissolve the oxide to a colorless solution. Localized heating is to be avoided because it gives colored solutions and impure products. The clear solution is placed in an ice bath and frozen. The frozen mass is allowed to warm to room temperature, the rhenium(VII) oxide–dioxane complex crystallizing out as a dense, pearl-gray deposit as the excess dioxane melts. The freezing

* Polytechnic Institute of Brooklyn, Brooklyn, N.Y.
† University of Illinois, Urbana, Ill.

and melting are repeated at least once to ensure separation of the complex. The colorless supernatant liquid containing only negligible amounts of rhenium is then removed by decantation. The complex is dried at room temperature over sulfuric acid in a vacuum desiccator.

The dry complex is transferred quickly to a crucible which is heated gently on a hot plate. The material is first melted to a colorless to blue-green liquid which decomposes to red rhenium(VI) oxide and volatile rhenium-free products as heating is continued. Reaction is complete in a few minutes. The product is chemically pure. The yield amounts to about 95 per cent of theory, some loss occurring because of the slight solubility of the complex in dioxane.

Procedure B

$$Re_2O_7 + CO \rightarrow 2ReO_3 + CO_2$$

SUBMITTED BY A. D. MELAVEN,[*] J. N. FOWLE,[*] W. BRICKELL,[*] AND C. F. HISKEY[*]

CHECKED BY THERALD MOELLER[†] AND R. L. BURTON[†]

The apparatus for the preparation of rhenium(VII) oxide (synthesis 50) is modified by interposing a short (2- to 3-mm.) section of 1-mm. capillary tubing between the reaction tube and the remainder of the apparatus as depicted in Fig. 39. One-tenth to one gram of rhenium metal is converted into rhenium(VII) oxide, which is purified by sublimation. Any nonvolatile residue remaining in the tip of the reaction tube is sealed off and detached. The reaction tube is bent from a horizontal to a vertical position as indicated in Fig. 38. The system is evacuated and filled with carbon monoxide[3] to a pressure of one atmosphere. The tube containing the rhenium(VII) oxide is slowly heated to 175° by means of a glycerol bath and is maintained at that temperature until the oxide is blue. The temperature is then raised slowly to 225°, and, after the preparation has turned red, is increased to 280°. The

* University of Tennessee, Knoxville, Tenn.
† University of Illinois, Urbana, Ill.

entire heating operation should last no more than 2 to 3 hours. The red product is pure ReO_3. Yield, quantitative.

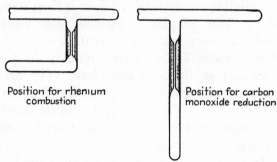

Position for rhenium
combustion

Position for carbon
monoxide reduction

FIG. 38.   Apparatus for preparation of rhenium(VI) oxide.   See also Fig. 39.

Properties

Rhenium(VI) oxide is a red solid, crystallizing in the cubic system. In thin layers, the oxide appears green by transmitted light. It is unreactive to water and to most reagents of nonoxidizing or reducing character. At 400°, it disproportionates in a vacuum to rhenium(IV) and rhenium(VII) oxides.

References

1. BILTZ, LEHRER, and MEISEL: *Z. anorg. allgem. Chem.*, **207**, 113 (1932).
2. BILTZ and LEHRER: *Z. anorg. allgem. Chem.*, **214**, 225 (1933).
3. GILLILAND and BLANCHARD: INORGANIC SYNTHESES, **2**, 81 (1946).

50. RHENIUM(VII) OXIDE

(Dirhenium Heptoxide)

$$4Re + 7O_2 \rightarrow 2Re_2O_7$$

SUBMITTED BY A. D. MELAVEN,* J. N. FOWLE,* WALTER BRICKELL,* AND C. F. HISKEY*
CHECKED BY THERALD MOELLER† AND R. L. BURTON†

Rhenium(VII) oxide can be prepared from the metal or from lower rhenium oxides by direct oxidation in a stream of air or oxygen.[1,2] When this is done, however, a variable

* University of Tennessee, Knoxville, Tenn.
† University of Illinois, Urbana, Ill.

amount of an uncondensable oxide of undetermined composition is produced as a white smoke along with the yellow oxide. By means of controlled oxidation in a closed system such difficulties may be avoided, and the preparation of small quantities of rhenium(VII) oxide effected easily.

Oxidation of the metal appears to proceed in two steps. The metal first ignites with a red glow. When this reaction subsides, a deposit of red rhenium(VI) oxide remains. Further oxidation as heating is continued then gives the volatile yellow rhenium(VII) oxide.

Procedure

Up to 2 g. of rhenium metal[3] is placed at the closed end of

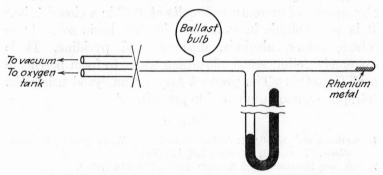

FIG. 39. Apparatus for preparation of rhenium(VII) oxide.

a pyrex tube 9 mm. in diameter and 20 cm. or more in length. This tube is then sealed in a horizontal position to an assembly of at least 1-l. capacity as shown in Fig. 39. A ballast bulb and a three-way stopcock are essential to the assembly. A closed-end manometer sealed to the apparatus is of convenience, particularly when larger amounts of rhenium are to be oxidized. The apparatus is evacuated and flamed to ensure complete dryness. It is then flushed with dry oxygen and filled with this gas to a pressure of 1 atmosphere. A short tubular furnace, previously heated to 400 to 425°, is slipped over the horizontal tube containing the rhenium so as to heat a 5-cm. length. After 2 hours of heating, the furnace is advanced another 5 cm. and heating

is continued for an additional 2 hours.   If the product in
the tube is not bright yellow, heating is continued as long
as is necessary.*   After the reaction is complete, the sublimed sample is preserved by sealing it off in the reaction
tube.

By this method it is possible to form the oxide and deposit
it wherever desired in a particular apparatus.   It is important to work with the combustion tube in a horizontal position.   In a vertical position the reaction time is lengthened
immeasurably.

Properties

Rhenium(VII) oxide is a canary-yellow solid, forming as
hexagonal crystals.   It begins to sublime at 250° under 1
atmosphere of pressure and melts at 297° in a closed tube.[5]
It is very soluble in water and in such basic solvents as
ethers, esters, alcohols, dioxane, and pyridine.   It is
extremely deliquescent, absorbing water to form perrhenic
acid ($HReO_4$).   The product may be analyzed using the
tetraphenylarsonium chloride procedure.[4]

References

1. NODDACK and NODDACK: *Naturwissenschaften*, **17**, 93 (1929); *Z. anorg.
   allgem. Chem.*, **181**, 1 (1929); **215**, 129 (1933).
2. BRISCOE, ROBINSON, and RUDGE: *Nature*, **129**, 618 (1932).
3. HURD and BRIMM: INORGANIC SYNTHESES, **1**, 175 (1939).
4. WILLARD and SMITH: *Anal. Chem.*, **11**, 305 (1939).
5. OGAWA: *Bull. Chem. Soc. Japan*, **7**, 265 (1932).

* Not more than 5 hours of heating should be required for 2 g. of the metal.

CHAPTER VIII

See also: Nickel(II) fluoride, synthesis 47A
Cobalt(III) flouride, synthesis 47B

51. ANHYDROUS IRON(III) CHLORIDE

(Ferric Chloride)

$$2Fe + 3Cl_2 \rightarrow 2FeCl_3$$

SUBMITTED BY BETTY RAPP TARR*
CHECKED BY HAROLD S. BOOTH† AND ALBERT DOLANCE†

The most convenient laboratory method for the preparation of iron(III) chloride involves the direct combustion of metallic iron in dry chlorine.[1] The directions given here are suitable for preparing this material in 100-g. quantities or, by simple modification of the apparatus, in larger amounts.

Iron(III) chloride has been employed as a catalyst in such reactions as the Friedel-Crafts synthesis,[2] the preparation of alkyl chlorides from olefins (other than ethylene), and the hydrogenation[3] and chlorination of aromatic compounds.[4]

Procedure A (Small Quantities)

The apparatus depicted in Fig. 40 is made of 28-mm. pyrex tubing and consists of a reaction chamber D and three collection chambers E, F, and G, each 25 cm. in length joined by 5-cm. constricted segments that should not be less than 10 mm. in diameter. Just before the reaction is carried out the tube is flamed, while a current of dry air is passed through it, to remove all moisture.

* University of Illinois, Urbana, Ill.
† Western Reserve University, Cleveland, Ohio.

Thirty-five and one-half grams of pure iron wire (No. 36)*
is dried at 110°, cooled in a desiccator and then placed in
the reaction chamber D. Chlorine gas is passed through
the sulfuric acid wash bottle A and through a drying tube
C containing phosphorus(V) oxide. Between these two
vessels, the train is provided with a side tube B dipping
into sulfuric acid to act as a safety outlet for the chlorine
in event the combustion tube becomes clogged. From C
the chlorine is passed through the combustion tube and
thence through a container of calcium chloride H to prevent
the entrance of moisture. The unreacted chlorine passes
through a trap I and is absorbed by sodium hydroxide in J.

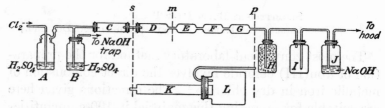

Fig. 40.   Apparatus for preparation of anhydrous iron(III) chloride.

After the air has been displaced with chlorine, the seg-
ment D containing the iron wire is heated gently. The
reaction takes place readily and iron(III) chloride soon
begins to fill the reaction chamber. After the reaction has
ceased, the product is sublimed by careful heating in an
atmosphere of chlorine from the reaction chamber into the
two succeeding segments E and F. Care is taken that none
of the constricted portions become clogged. The flow of
chlorine is stopped and the tube sealed off at the point m.
The opposite end of the tube at p is now attached to the
vacuum line through a sodium hydroxide trap and the
excess of chlorine is removed. The tube is then sealed at p.
The anhydrous chloride is then distributed by sublimation
into the tubes as desired. If it is desired to collect the
total yield in one compartment, the end segments may be

* Finer wire should not be used, as the reaction is apt to become too
vigorous.

heated in an electric tube furnace and each one may be sealed off after it has been emptied. The yield is nearly quantitative. Since it is difficult to sublime the last bit of iron(III) chloride completely from the reaction chamber, there is usually about a 3 per cent loss at this point. The material is not absolutely pure, as it contains small amounts of iron(II) chloride, but is suitable for most work. An absolutely pure product may be obtained by repeated sublimation in an atmosphere of chlorine.

Procedure B (Larger Quantities)

That portion of the apparatus from *s* to *p* is replaced by a pyrex combustion tube *K* connected through a rubber stopper to a wide-mouthed bottle *L* (which, after removal from the apparatus, can be closed with a ground-glass stopper). This bottle should be thoroughly dried in an oven at 125° before the synthesis is carried out. The reaction tube *K* is flamed while dry air is passed through it. For 70 g. of iron wire, a 1-l. bottle should be used. Number 36 iron wire is employed, as before. The iron(III) chloride, as it is formed, is sublimed into the bottle.

The excess chlorine is conducted to trap *H* through a tube that should be at least 1 cm. in diameter. When the reaction is complete, the bottle *L* is disconnected from the apparatus and immediately stoppered.

Properties

Anhydrous iron(III) chloride forms crystals that are dark green in reflected light and purple-red in transmitted light. The compound melts at 306° and can be volatilized at a slightly lower temperature. Vapor density measurements show that iron(III) chloride is dimeric at 440°, but monomeric above 750°. Measurements at these higher temperatures are complicated by the fact that appreciable dissociation into iron(II) chloride and chlorine also takes place. On exposure to air the anhydrous salt is readily transformed to the yellow-brown 6-hydrate. Accordingly, if it is necessary to transfer the anhydrous material from one vessel to another, the operation should be carried out in a "dry box," or according to the procedure described by Bergstrom.[1]

Anhydrous iron(III) chloride is soluble in many solvents, especially those which can coordinate with it, such as the alcohols, ethers, ketones, pyridine, benzonitrile, phosphorus(III) bromide, sulfur dioxide, and sulfuryl chloride.

References

1. BERGSTROM: *J. Am. Chem. Soc.*, **46**, 1547 (1924).
2. GALLAY and WHITBY: *Can. J. Research*, **2**, 31 (1930).
3. KLING and FLORENTIN: *Compt. rend.*, **184**, 822 (1927).
4. MASON, SMALE, THOMPSON, and WHEELER: *J. Chem. Soc.*, **1931**, 3150.

52. HEXAMMINENICKEL(II) BROMIDE AND HEXAMMINENICKEL(II) IODIDE

$$[Ni(OH)_2]_4 \cdot H_2O + 8HX \rightarrow 4NiX_2 + 9H_2O$$
$$NiX_2 + 6NH_3 \rightarrow [Ni(NH_3)_6]X_2$$

SUBMITTED BY GEORGE W. WATT*
CHECKED BY R. KEITH OSTERHELD†

The hexammines of the bromide and iodide of nickel(II) provide a convenient means of introducing nickel(II) ion into liquid ammonia solutions under anhydrous conditions.[1,2] Although the literature includes numerous references to the preparation of these compounds from the corresponding anhydrous salts or their hydrates,[2-4] details of procedure have not been specified. The simple procedure outlined below provides these salts in high yield and high purity.

Procedure

Twenty grams of reagent-grade hydrated nickel(II) hydroxide,‡ $[Ni(OH)_2]_4 \cdot H_2O$, is dissolved in 55 ml. of warm

* The University of Texas, Austin, Tex.
† The University of Illinois, Urbana, Ill.
‡ If the solid hydroxide is not available, it may be prepared conveniently by precipitation from a solution of a nickel(II) salt such as the sulfate by addition of sodium hydroxide, followed by thorough washing.

constant-boiling hydrobromic acid solution (b.p. 126°; d. 1.47; 47.5 per cent HBr).* If any unreacted solid remains, it is removed by filtration. To the filtrate is added an additional 3 ml. of hydrobromic acid solution and enough water to bring the total volume to 150 ml. This solution is added dropwise over a period of 20 to 25 minutes to 550 ml. of concentrated aqueous ammonia solution previously heated to 65 to 70°. The solution is maintained at this temperature throughout the addition of the nickel(II) bromide solution; stirring and saturation with respect to ammonia are accomplished by bubbling through the solution a vigorous stream of ammonia gas from a commercial cylinder. Pale violet-colored crystals of hexamminenickel(II) bromide begin to separate from the solution before the addition of the bromide solution is complete.

Crystallization is completed by cooling the reaction mixture in an ice bath. The yield may be increased slightly by continuing the addition of ammonia gas until the solution is saturated at the lower temperature. The crystals are removed by filtration, washed five times with 50-ml. portions of cold 26 per cent aqueous ammonia. Yield, 63 g. or 95 per cent. *Anal.* Calcd. for $Ni(NH_3)_6Br_2$: Ni, 18.30; Br, 49.84; NH_3, 31.86. Found: Ni, 18.28; Br, 49.67; NH_3, 31.90. Calcd. for $Ni(NH_3)_6I_2$: Ni, 14.15; I, 61.25; NH_3, 24.64. Found: Ni, 14.11; I, 61.58; NH_3, 23.94.

Properties

The hexamminenickel(II) bromide and iodide separate in the form of face-centered cubic crystals that are isomorphous with ammonium hexachloroplatinate(IV). Depending upon particle size, the color of the crystals varies from pale lavender to deep blue. The bromide is soluble in hot water and may be recrystallized from concentrated aqueous ammonia. These salts should be stored in tightly stop-

* Although freshly distilled constant-boiling acid is recommended, its concentration is not critical. Thus, the bromide has been prepared satisfactorily using 68.8 ml. of 40 per cent hydrobromic acid (d. 1.38). Similarly, the iodide has been formed using 87 ml. of 47 per cent hydriodic acid (d. 1.50).

pered bottles to minimize atmospheric oxidation. The iodide is considerably less soluble in water than the bromide and both are sparingly soluble in liquid ammonia. Both salts are decomposed by bases and are converted to nickel(II) hydroxide by boiling with water. Thermal dissociation of the hexamminenickel(II) bromide yields successively compounds containing 2, 1, 0 mols of ammonia. The corresponding iodide is less stable and loses ammonia to form the diammine, and finally the unsolvated iodide.

References

1. BURGESS and EASTES: *J. Am. Chem. Soc.*, **63**, 2674 (1941).
2. WATT and DAVIES: *ibid.*, **70**, 3753 (1948).
3. RICHARDS and CUSHMAN: *Z. anorg. Chem.*, **16**, 167 (1898).
4. RAMMELSBERG: *Pogg. Ann.*, **48**, 119, 155 (1839); **55**, 243 (1846).
5. ERDMAN: *J. prakt. Chem.*, [1] **1**, 266 (1834); [1] **7**, 249 (1836).

53. BIS(N,N'-DISALICYLALETHYLENEDIAMINE)-μ-AQUODICOBALT(II)

{Bis[N,N'-bis(o-hydroxybenzylidine)ethylenediamine]-μ-aquodicobalt(II)}

$$2C_{16}H_{16}N_2O_2 + 2CoCl_2 + 4NaOH \rightarrow$$
$$\{[Co(C_{16}H_{14}N_2O_2)]_2H_2O\} + 4NaCl + 3H_2O$$

SUBMITTED BY HARVEY DIEHL* AND CLIFFORD C. HACH*
CHECKED BY JOHN C. BAILAR, JR.†

* Iowa State College, Ames, Iowa.
† University of Illinois, Urbana, Ill.

The cobalt(II) derivative of *N,N'*-disalicylalethylene-diamine, a Schiff base prepared from salicylaldehyde and ethylenediamine, was first described by Pfeiffer, Breith, Lübbe, and Tsumaki[1] and further studied by Tsumaki.[2] It was later investigated intensively by Diehl and coworkers,[3] who showed that it is a binuclear compound in which a molecule of water acts as a bridging group (μ-aquo) between two cobalt atoms, each of which is surrounded by the quadridentate, chelating molecule of the Schiff base. This material has the unique property of reversibly absorbing and releasing oxygen. The addition of the oxygen is thought to take place by the formation of a peroxo group, which makes a second bridge between the two cobalt atoms and fills the sixth coordination position of each cobalt atom. Thus, one oxygen molecule is absorbed for each two cobalt atoms, corresponding to a gain in weight of 4.79 per cent.

The compound was originally prepared by bringing cobalt acetate, ethylenediamine, and salicylaldehyde together simultaneously in an aqueous-alcohol reaction medium. Unless care is exercised in this procedure the product is relatively impure, but if all the factors mentioned below are controlled, a satisfactory material can be obtained by this direct mixing method. A much better procedure involves the preliminary formation of the Schiff base and its subsequent reaction with a cobalt salt. In this manner a product is obtained containing the correct stoichiometric ratio of salicylaldehyde to ethylenediamine; slight departure from the equivalent quantities or inadequate stirring in the direct mixing method leads to contamination of the product by the cobalt derivative of salicylaldehyde, by cobalt-ethylenediamine compounds, or by the Schiff base.

The recommended synthesis is complicated under certain conditions by the formation of three by-products, olive, black, and red in color, all of which are inactive toward oxygen. The olive by-product is formed on prolonged contact of the oxygen-carrying material with hot water, either during the formation of the material or during drying. The presence of any free acid, especially when hot, promotes the formation of this olive by-product. A critical point in the procedure is, therefore, the drying step, which must be carried out as rapidly as possible.

The black by-product is formed from the oxygen-carrying compound by contact with oxygen, especially in the presence of alcohol; its formation is not observed in the procedure given here. It is soluble in water and removed by washing. The red by-product results from the action of alkali on the oxygen-carrying compound. In the procedure given below, a slight deficiency of alkali is used to avoid its formation. It is isomeric with the oxygen-carrying compound, but inactive toward oxygen.

Procedure

N,N′-Disalicylalethylenediamine. The salicylaldehyde is purified by the process of shaking or by standing in contact with powdered calcium carbonate, followed by distillation. To a solution of 244 g. (2 mols) of the purified material in 1 l. of boiling 95 per cent ethyl alcohol is added 60.1 g. (1 mol) of ethylenediamine; this is measured by weighing out the appropriate amount of aqueous solution. If the concentration of the ethylenediamine is not known within a few per cent, a sample should be titrated against a standard acid, using methyl red as indicator. In 20 to 30 seconds the mass becomes solid with formation of a bright yellow, crystalline material. The reaction mixture is cooled and filtered on a Büchner funnel, and the precipitate is spread in thin layers on absorbent paper to dry. It may be recrystallized from 6 l. of hot 95 per cent alcohol or used without further purification. It will dissolve somewhat more readily in the next step if it is not allowed to dry completely. Yield, 255 g. (95 per cent). The compound melts at 123°.

Bis(*N,N′*-disalicylalethylenediamine)-μ-aquodicobalt. One mol (268 g.) of finely ground disalicylalethylenediamine, 79.5 g. (2 mols less 0.5 g.) of sodium hydroxide and 5 g. of sodium acetate, $NaC_2H_3O_2 \cdot 3H_2O$, are dissolved in 3 l. of boiling water. Solution of the disalicylalethylenediamine requires from 10 to 20 minutes and depends on the state of subdivision of the material and the agitation given the mixture. Stirring is continued subsequently while a solution of 238 g. (1 mol) of hexahydrated cobalt(II) chloride ($CoCl_2 \cdot 6H_2O$) in 500 ml. of hot water is added, until the mixture sets up to a reddish-brown paste. The mass is covered with ½ in. of water and allowed to stand for at least 15 minutes. It is then centrifuged* until most of the mother liquor has been removed and a hard cake remains. Three portions of water (each about 250 ml.) are added, the liquid being removed by centrifugation after each addition. The cake is removed from the centrifuge basket and mixed thoroughly with 1.5 l. of water so that no large particles remain and a uniform slurry is obtained. It is centrifuged again, and is finally washed with a few hundred milliliters of water. The filtrate will never be colorless, but will be light brown. The cake is finally centrifuged as dry as possible. If a letter press† is available, the cake should be wrapped in a few thicknesses of towel and pressed. It is then broken into small pieces and dried at 100° in a good vacuum. The final vacuum drying apparatus need not be complicated but should be provided with a large gas outlet and a condenser to allow adequate facility for the escape of steam. Direct connection to a water pump is poor inasmuch as a water pump cannot handle a sufficiently large volume of vapor. A satisfactory drier may be constructed from pyrex tubing, 2 in. in diam-

* If a centrifuge is not available, suction filtration may be substituted. However, the residual water left on the cake is less when a material is centrifuged than when filtered by suction, so the use of a centrifuge is much to be preferred. The centrifuge of the International Equipment Company, No. 418, with a bronze basket is ideal for the purpose.

† The use of a hydraulic press is desirable if the material has been separated by centrifuging and almost necessary if it is separated by suction filtration.

eter and 36 in. long.   This tube is surrounded by a second
pyrex tube 3 in. in diameter and just slightly shorter, which
serves as a jacket through which steam can be passed.
The inner tube can be supported concentrically in the outer
tube at one end by a few turns of rubber tubing of suitable
diameter, which also serves as a steam inlet.   At the other
end, a single turn of rubber tubing can be used, leaving a
gap at the bottom for the condensate to escape.   The
material is placed in the inner tube on a tray made by
bending a strip of tin plate into a semicircular cross section.
One end of this tube is stoppered and the other connected
through a tube 0.75 in. in diameter to a condenser, receiver,
and water pump.   The condenser and receiver may consist
simply of a 1-l. round-bottomed flask cooled by a stream of
running water.   The yield is 300 g., or 90 per cent; oxygen-
carrying capacity, 4.7 to 4.8 per cent; theoretical capacity,
4.79 per cent.*

Properties

Bis(N,N'-disalicylalethylenediamine)-μ-aquodicobalt is a
maroon-colored, microcrystalline material, which is somewhat soluble in pyridine, chloroform, and benzene.   It
crystallizes from pyridine and chloroform with solvent of
crystallization that can be removed by heating at 120° in a
vacuum; the resulting product, however, is of low oxygen-
carrying capacity.   The material absorbs oxygen in the
dry state, turning from maroon to black in color.   The rate
of oxygenation of the material is greatly affected by pressure
and temperature, being a maximum with respect to tem-

* The oxygen-carrying capacity of the material is determined by exposing
a weighed sample on a boat to oxygen or air at increased pressure and obtain-
ing the increase in weight.   This is best carried out in a metal tube equipped
with a screw cap, pressure gage, line to oxygen tank or air line, and release
valve.   A period of 10 minutes in oxygen at 100 pounds pressure is sufficient
to saturate the compound, after which the pressure may be released and the
boat weighed rapidly.   It is usually necessary to deoxygenate the material
at 100° in a vacuum to secure a correct initial weight of the sample.   The
maximum oxygen-carrying capacity is obtained after two or three cycles of
oxygenation and deoxygenation.

perature at about 20°. The oxygen is expelled by heating the material to 65°. It also absorbs nitrogen(II) oxide and nitrogen(IV) oxide, but irreversibly. It does not absorb carbon monoxide, nitrous oxide, or sulfur dioxide. The deoxygenated form of the material is paramagnetic, the oxygenated form diamagnetic. It catalyzes the luminescence of 3-aminophthalhydrazide (luminol) in alkaline solution containing hydrogen peroxide. The compound is quite toxic; inhalation of the finely divided dust should be avoided.

References

1. PFEIFFER, BREITH, LÜBBE, and TSUMAKI: *Ann.,* **503,** 84 (1933).
2. TSUMAKI: *Bull. Chem. Soc. Japan,* **13,** 252 (1938).
3. DIEHL and co-workers: "Studies on Oxygen-carrying Cobalt Compounds," Iowa State College, Ames, Iowa, (1946).

INDEX OF CONTRIBUTORS

SUBJECT INDEX

Names employed in the cumulative subject index for Volumes I, II, and III are based upon those adopted in Volume II (Appendix, page 257) with a few changes that have been standardized and approved since publication of Volume II. Some of the general principles that have been followed in setting up the index are (1) The Stock system, based on the use of Roman numerals to designate oxidation state, has been generally preferred; for example, *Iron(III) chloride*, rather than ferric chloride; *Potassium hexachlorohenate(IV)* rather than potassium chlorohenite. (2) In the case of heteropoly acids, the structure-determining element is named last, as for instance, *12-Tungstophosphoric acid*. (3) General headings such as *Chromium(III) complex compounds* and *Ammines* are employed for grouping coordination compounds of similar types. In addition, entries are made under the specific names for individual compounds. (Halogeno and cyano complexes, however, have been entered only under their specific names.) (4) Numerical prefixes and prefixes such as "ortho-" and "meta-" (but not "hypo-" and "per-") have been dropped at the beginnings of names to form general headings covering classes of compounds such as *Silicon chlorides* and *Phosphoric acids*. (5) Formulas for specific compounds are used under general headings. The Formula Index should also prove particularly helpful in troublesome cases. (6) Because of changes in practice since the appearance of Volume I, it has been deemed advisable to make extra entries or cross references under names that have been changed and also under many specific names for compounds entered under general headings (cf. 4 above). (7) Two entries are made for compounds having two cations. (8) Unsatisfactory names that have been retained for want of better ones are placed in quotation marks.

Inverted names are used only for derivatives of silanes (as *Silane, dibromo-;* and *Disilane, hexachloro-*) and germanes, but not for the few organic compounds.

Headings are alphabeted straight through, letter by letter, as in *Chemical Abstracts*, not word by word. Roman numerals in Stock names are ignored unless two or more names are otherwise the same.

A

Acetic acid, glacial, dehydration for use in preparation of titanium derivative of acetylacetone, **2** :119

Acetic acid-acetic anhydride solution, **1** :85

Acetylacetone, metal derivatives of, **2** :14, 17, 25, 119, 121, 123

   metal derivatives of, nomenclature of, **2** :16

   structure of, **2** :10

Acetylene, purification of, **2** :76

Acids, nomenclature of isopoly and heteropoly, **2** :263

FORMULA INDEX

The chief aim of this formula index, like that of other formula indexes, is to help in locating specific compounds, or even groups of compounds, that might not be easily found in the Subject Index. To this end, formulas have been used wherever it seemed best in their usual form (*i.e.*, as used in the text) for easy recognition, PbO_2, $EuSO_4$, Si_2Cl_6, $ThOBr_2$. However, for compounds containing the more uncommon elements and groupings and also for complexes, the significant or central atom has been placed first in the formula in order to throw together as many related compounds as possible. This procedure usually involves placing the cation last (often of relatively minor interest, especially in the case of alkali and alkaline earth metals): $PtCl_4K_2$; $[Al(C_2O_4)_3]K_3 \cdot 3H_2O$; $(IO_6)_2Ba_3H_4$. The guiding principle in these cases has been the chapter in the text in which the preparation of the compound is described. Where there is likely to be almost equal interest in two or more parts of a formula, two or more entries have been made: $AgClO_3$ and ClO_3Ag; Al_2Se_3 and Se_3Al_2; SF_6 and F_6S (simple halides other than fluorides are entered only under the other element in most cases); $NaNH_2$ and NH_2Na; NH_2SO_3H and SO_3HNH_2.

Formulas for organic compounds are structural or semistructural: $CH_3COCH_2COCH_3$. Consideration has been given to probable interest by inorganic chemists, *i.e.*, any element other than carbon, hydrogen, or oxygen in an organic molecule is given priority in the formula if only one entry is made, or equal rating if more than one entry: $Zr(C_5H_7O_2)_4 \cdot 10H_2O$; $NaC \equiv CH$ and $CH \equiv CNa$.

The names used with the formulas are the preferred specific names.

The formulas are listed alphabetically by atoms or by groups (considered as units) and then according to the number of each in turn in the formula rather than by total number of atoms of each element. This system results in arrangements such as the following:

$NH_2SO_3NH_4$
$(NH_2)_2C_2H_4$ (instead of $N_2H_4C_2H_4$, $N_2H_8C_2$, or $C_2H_8N_2$)
NH_3

$Si(CH_3)Cl_3$
$Si(CH_3)_3Cl$
$Si(CH=CH_2)Cl_3$
$Si(C_2H_4Cl)Cl_3$

$Cr(CN)_6K_3$ (instead of $CrC_6N_6K_3$)
$Cr(C_2H_3O_2)_2$ (instead of $CrC_4H_6O_4$)
$[Cr(C_2O_4)_3]K_3 \cdot 3H_2O$ (instead of $CrC_6O_{12}K_3 \cdot H_6O_3$ or $CrC_6O_{15}K_3H_6$)
$[Cr(en)_2Cl_2]Cl \cdot H_2O$ ("en" is retained for simplicity and is alphabeted as such rather than as $C_2H_4(NH_2)_2$ or $(NH_2)_2C_2H_4$)

221